AS/A-LEVEL

Physics

Mike Crundell

ESSENTIAL WORD
DICTIONARY

Philip Allan Updates
Market Place
Deddington
Oxfordshire
OX15 0SE

Tel: 01869 338652
Fax: 01869 337590
e-mail: sales@philipallan.co.uk
www.philipallan.co.uk

ISBN 0 86003 377 5

Acknowledgement
Every effort has been made to eliminate errors and omissions in the
text. To this end, I would like to thank Dr Chris Mee for his helpful
advice and for his careful reading of the manuscript.

Printed by Raithby Lawrence & Co Ltd, Leicester

Introduction

In a dictionary of this size, it is not possible to include *all* the terms you are likely to meet in your study of AS or A-level physics. Instead, only important terms have been included. This will help you to learn key facts more efficiently and to acquire a better understanding of the subject.

In the dictionary, each term is defined in up to four parts:

(1) a brief definition
(2) further explanation of the term
(3) an example, where relevant
(4) an examiner's tip, such as where the term is commonly misunderstood, confused with another term, used in error or found in conjunction with other terms.

In many cases, all four parts are not needed and the entry has been modified accordingly.

For each term it may be necessary to make a cross-reference to words shown in italics in order to understand fully the entry you are reading. Cross-referencing helps with understanding the association between different aspects of the subject. To do well in physics, you need to appreciate these links rather than learn a large number of isolated ideas.

Finally, appendices A–C on pages 161–164 provide tables of important quantities, symbols and units, formulae and equations, as well as physical constants and other useful data.

absolute scale of temperature: see *thermodynamic scale of temperature.*

absolute zero of temperature: the temperature at which any object has minimum internal energy; it is the zero of the *thermodynamic scale of temperature.*

■ This temperature is zero kelvin (0 K) or –273.15 degrees Celsius (°C). For an ideal gas, the energy of its atoms is zero at absolute zero.

■ *TIP* In many calculations at AS/A-level, three significant figure accuracy is ample and thus the conversion factor between kelvin and degrees Celsius is taken as 273, rather than 273.15.

absorption coefficient: see *attenuation.*

absorption spectrum, line: the spectrum produced when light from a hot body passes through a cooler gas; it appears as a series of separate dark lines on a *continuous spectrum.*

■ The spectrum shows the colours (wavelengths) of electromagnetic radiation absorbed by atoms of cool gas when electrons in these atoms move from their *ground states* to *excited states*. The lines are the images of the slit at the front of the instrument used to split the light into its separate wavelengths. When an electron in its ground state of energy E_1 absorbs a photon and moves to an excited state of energy E_2, the photon absorbed has frequency f and wavelength λ given by

$$E_2 - E_1 = hf = hc/\lambda$$

where h is the *Planck constant* and c is the speed of light.

■ *e.g.* Absorption spectra may be used to identify gases in the outer layers of a star.

■ *TIP* Note that only specific wavelengths are missing from an absorption spectrum because an absorbed photon must have just the right energy to excite the electron from its ground state to an excited state. Photons not having this correct energy will not be absorbed.

acceleration: the rate of change of velocity with respect to time.

■ It is defined by the word equation

$$\text{acceleration} = \frac{\text{change in velocity}}{\text{time taken}}$$

The SI unit of acceleration is metre per second squared (m s^{-2}). Since *velocity* is a *vector quantity*, acceleration is also a vector. The magnitude of an acceleration is given by the *gradient* of a velocity–time graph.

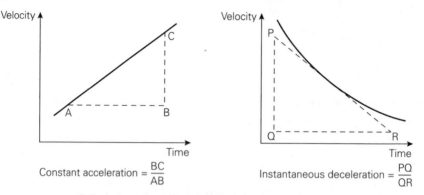

Calculation of acceleration from a velocity–time graph

For an object with a constant acceleration a, increasing its velocity from u to v in time t gives

$$a = \frac{v - u}{t}$$

or

$$v = u + at$$

This equation is one of the three *equations of uniformly accelerated motion*. A negative acceleration implies that a body is slowing down in the direction in which it is moving, and is referred to as a *deceleration* or a *retardation*.

■ **TIP** The equation $v = u + at$ applies only to a constant or uniform acceleration. Remember that an acceleration has a positive sign, while a deceleration or retardation has a negative sign.

acceleration of free fall: the *acceleration* of a body towards the surface of the Earth when the only force acting on it is its *weight*.

■ The acceleration of free fall (usual symbol g) depends on location on the Earth's surface and also on altitude. For the purpose of calculations, the generally accepted value for g is 9.81 m s^{-2}.

■ **TIP** In an examination, you may be asked to describe a free-fall method for the determination of g. Do not be tempted to describe a method using a pendulum or a spring; these methods do not involve free fall and will score no marks!

accuracy: the closeness of a reading on an instrument to the true value of the quantity being measured.

▨ An accurate instrument will give readings close to the true values.

▨ **TIP** Do not confuse accuracy with *precision*. An instrument may be accurate (give readings close to the true values) but still be imprecise if it does not have small scale divisions.

activity: when referring to a radioactive source, activity is the number of nuclear disintegrations per unit time.

▨ The SI unit of activity is the becquerel (Bq), where 1 Bq is one disintegration per second: $1\,\text{Bq} = 1\,\text{s}^{-1}$. Activity used to be measured in curies (Ci), where $1\,\text{Ci} = 3.7 \times 10^{10}\,\text{Bq}$.

▨ **TIP** Activity should not be confused with count rate. Whereas activity is a measure of rate of disintegration, count rate is concerned with rate of detection of particles or photons.

α-decay: see *alpha decay*.

adiabatic change: a change in the pressure, volume and temperature of a system such that, during the change, no thermal energy enters or leaves the system.

▨ According to the *first law of thermodynamics*, this means that any work done by the system is seen as a reduction in its internal energy or vice versa. In practice, any change that takes place suddenly is likely to be adiabatic.

alpha decay: the spontaneous decay of a nucleus with the emission of an *alpha particle*.

▨ Since an alpha particle is a helium (^4_2He) nucleus, the decay of nucleus X to nucleus Y may be represented by

$$^A_Z\text{X} \longrightarrow ^{A-4}_{Z-2}\text{Y} + ^4_2\text{He} + \text{energy}$$

Frequently, some of the energy released in the decay is seen as a gamma ray photon.

▨ **TIP** Remember that it is the parent nucleus that is radioactive, not the alpha particle.

alpha particle: a particle that may be emitted from a radioactive nucleus.

▨ An alpha particle (α-particle) contains two protons and two neutrons and is the same as a helium nucleus (^4_2He). It has a charge of $+2e$ and mass $4u$. Alpha particles have energies up to several MeV and travel at speeds up to $0.1\,c$ when emitted from a nucleus but, owing to their comparatively large charge and mass, they rapidly lose energy through *ionisation* and thus have low penetration in matter. The path length (penetration) of alpha particles in air is a few centimetres. They are stopped by a sheet of thick paper.

▨ **TIP** It is the source of alpha particles that is radioactive; not the alpha particles themselves.

alpha particle scattering experiment: the experiment carried out by Geiger and Marsden under the direction of Rutherford that provided evidence for the existence, charge and small size of the nucleus.

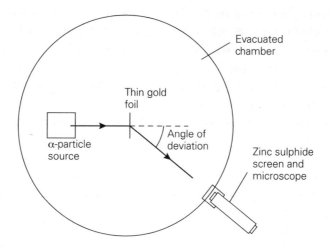

■ The parallel beam of alpha particles was incident on a thin gold foil that was only about 100 atoms thick. The alpha particles were deflected by the foil and detected as small flashes of light (scintillations) on a zinc sulphide screen viewed with a low-power microscope. The apparatus was enclosed in an evacuated vessel. The following observations were made:

- the majority of alpha particles passed through the foil with little or no deviation
- a small fraction (about 1 in 10^4) of the alpha particles were deviated through angles greater than 90°

The outcome of the experiments verified Rutherford's nuclear model of the atom. Namely:

- the majority of the volume of an atom is empty space (most alpha particles suffered small deviations)
- at the centre of the atom is a very small, but dense, charged core, called the nucleus (large deviations of a small number of alpha particles)

Subsequent experiments showed that the nucleus is positively charged. (See also *Rutherford model of the atom*; *nucleus*.)

alpha radiation: the outward movement of *alpha particles* from a radioactive source.

■ The alpha particles carry energy from the source and cause *ionisation* of the medium through which they travel.

alternating current or voltage: term usually used in connection with the mains supply and restricted to a sinusoidal variation of current or voltage with time.

■ The values of the current I and the voltage V at time t are given by

$$I = I_0\sin 2\pi ft = I_0\sin\omega t$$
$$V = V_0\sin 2\pi ft = V_0\sin\omega t$$

where I_0 and V_0 are the peak or maximum values of the current and voltage, respectively, f is the frequency and ω (= $2\pi f$) is the angular frequency. The period T of the current or voltage is equal to $1/f$.

■ *TIP* Remember that the equations could be given in terms of cosine, rather than sine. The difference between the two would be concerned with the phase.

ammeter: an instrument used to measure electric current.

■ Ammeters may be digital or analogue. The ammeter is placed in series with the component through which the current is to be measured, as in the first diagram below (note the circuit symbol for an ammeter). Sensitive ammeters, designed to measure currents of the order of microamperes, are sometimes called galvanometers. The symbol for a centre-reading galvanometer is shown in the second diagram.

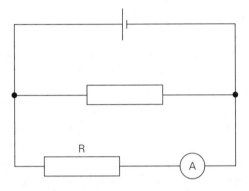

Ammeter connected to measure the current through R

Circuit symbol for a centre-reading galvanometer

amount of substance: the ratio of the number of discrete particles (atoms or molecules) of a substance to the number of atoms in 0.012 kg of carbon-12.

■ Amount of substance is measured in *moles* (mol). The number of discrete particles (atoms or molecules) in one mole of substance is known as the *Avogadro constant* (symbol N_A or L). The mole is one of the base quantities.

amp: see *ampere*.

ampere, A (also called 'amp'): the unit of electric current in the *SI system* of units.

■ It is one of the seven *base units* and is defined in terms of the force between two long, straight, parallel wires. In the diagram below, the current in one wire is situated in the magnetic field produced by the current in the other wire. Hence, by the *motor effect*, there is a force acting on each of the wires which depends, in part, on the size of the current in each wire.

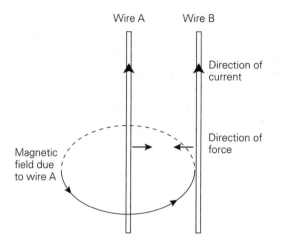

Force between two wires

By definition, if two long straight parallel conductors of negligible cross-sectional area are situated 1 m apart in a vacuum, and if the force per unit length acting on each wire is $2 \times 10^{-7}\,\mathrm{N\,m^{-1}}$, then the current in each wire is 1 ampere.

■ *TIP* Some examination specifications (syllabuses) do not require you to learn this definition. However, you are expected to understand the basis of the definition. Remember that electric current is defined in terms of the force between parallel current-carrying conductors, not as rate of flow of charge. The equation $\Delta Q = I\Delta t$ is used to define electric charge.

amplitude: the maximum displacement of an oscillating particle from its mean position.

■ Amplitude is a scalar quantity and is one of the defining quantities for simple harmonic motion or for a wave. For a particle undergoing simple harmonic motion, the amplitude a_0 may be shown on a displacement–time graph. The SI unit of amplitude is the metre (m).

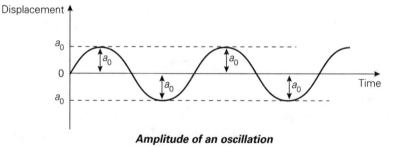

Amplitude of an oscillation

■ *TIP* Amplitude is the distance from a peak or from a trough to the mean position; it is not the peak-to-trough distance.

angular displacement: the angle through which an object turns, usually measured in radians (rad).

■ Angular displacement is a vector quantity and so the direction of rotation must be stated. The angular displacement in the diagram is θ rad in an anticlockwise direction.

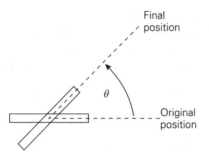

angular frequency: a measurement related to the *frequency* of a sinusoidal motion; it is measured in radians per second (rad s^{-1}).

■ For a sinusoidal motion of frequency f, the angular frequency ω is given by

$$\omega = 2\pi f$$

(See also *simple harmonic motion*.)

■ **TIP** Do not be tempted to use the unit s^{-1} for angular frequency. Frequency is measured in hertz or s^{-1}.

angular speed: the rate of change with time of the angular direction of the line joining an object to the axis about which it is rotating; it is measured in radians per second (rad s^{-1}).

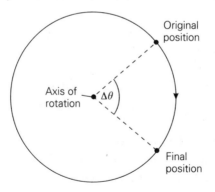

■ If the line rotates through angle $\Delta\theta$ in time Δt, the angular speed ω is given by

$$\omega = \Delta\theta/\Delta t$$

For an object completing f revolutions per unit time, the angular speed is given by

$$\omega = 2\pi f$$

since there are 2π rad in one revolution. Also, from the definition of the radian, arc length = radius × angle. If the object moves through the arc in time Δt, then dividing both sides of the equation by Δt gives speed along arc = radius × angular speed, i.e.

$$v = r\omega \text{ or } \omega = v/r$$

(See also *centripetal acceleration; centripetal force*.)

▧ *TIP* The equation $v = r\omega$ is important as it links angular speed with the linear speed of an object moving in a circular arc of radius r.

angular velocity: the angular speed in a given direction, usually either clockwise or anticlockwise; it is measured in radians per second (rad s^{-1}).

▧ Angular velocity is a *vector quantity*.

▧ *TIP* The term angular velocity is often used when, strictly speaking, reference should be made to *angular speed*.

antimatter: see *antiparticle*.

antinode: a point on a *stationary wave* where the amplitude of vibration is maximum.

▧ The distance between two neighbouring antinodes is equal to one half *wavelength* of the stationary wave.

antiparticle: each nuclear particle (*proton, neutron, electron*, etc.) appears to have an antiparticle with the same properties (e.g. mass) as the corresponding particle but with the opposite charge.

▧ Antiparticles are frequently created when high-energy particles are made to collide with one another. Their lifetimes are short because, when they encounter the equivalent particle, the particle and the antiparticle are annihilated. Their mass is seen as high-energy *gamma ray* photons.

antiphase: two waves or oscillations are in antiphase when the *phase difference* between them is 180° or π rad.

α-particle: see *alpha particle*.

apparent weight: the weight of an object when it is weighed in a fluid.

▧ According to *Archimedes' principle*, there is an *upthrust* acting on every object immersed in a fluid such that

apparent weight = weight in a vacuum − upthrust

For an object of volume V and density ρ, totally immersed in a fluid of density ρ_0, the apparent weight of the object is given by

apparent weight = $V(\rho - \rho_0)g$

where g is the acceleration of free fall.

▧ *TIP* If $\rho \gg \rho_0$, then the apparent weight is approximately equal to the actual weight. This would be the case, for example, for a lump of metal in air.

α-radiation: see *alpha radiation*.

Archimedes' principle: Archimedes' principle states that when an object is totally or partially immersed in a fluid, it experiences an upward force (*upthrust*) equal to the weight of fluid displaced.

■ The upthrust results from the difference in *fluid pressure* between the upper and lower surfaces of the object.

■ **e.g.** Archimedes' principle is important when considering *apparent weight*, flotation and *Millikan's oil drop experiment*.

■ *TIP* It is often forgotten that air is a fluid and, as a result, when an object is weighed in air, the measurement is not the true weight. However, for many objects the upthrust is much less than the actual weight and consequently the upthrust can be ignored. When the upthrust is similar to or greater than the actual weight, as in a hot air balloon, it cannot be ignored.

astronomical unit, AU: the average distance between the Earth and the sun — approximately 1.5×10^{11} m.

■ The astronomical unit is a convenient unit for measuring distances within the solar system. Other units of distance used in astrophysics are the *light-year* and the *parsec*.

atomic mass constant: see *unified atomic mass constant*.

atomic mass unit: a unit of mass equal to one-sixteenth of the mass of an atom of oxygen-16.

■ This unit has now been replaced by the *unified atomic mass unit*.

atomic number: see *proton number*.

attenuation: the reduction of the number of particles, or of the number of *photons*, in a beam as a result of the beam passing through a material.

■ For a parallel beam of initial *intensity I_0*, the intensity I after passing through a thickness x of material is given by

$$I = I_0 e^{-\mu x}$$

where μ is a constant known as the attenuation coefficient or absorption coefficient and is measured in m^{-1} (the SI unit). Alternative units are cm^{-1} and mm^{-1}, etc. The equation is also applicable to, for example, the absorption of beta particles or X-ray or gamma ray photons. The magnitude of the coefficient depends on the absorber and also on the energy of the particles or photons.

■ *TIP* A low attenuation coefficient corresponds to a high penetrating power.

attenuation coefficient: see *attenuation*.

Avogadro constant: the number of atoms in 0.012 kg of carbon-12; its symbol is N_A or L.

■ Since 0.012 kg of carbon-12 is one *mole* of substance, then the Avogadro constant is the number of discrete particles (atoms or molecules) in 1 mole of any substance. The value of the Avogadro constant is 6.02×10^{23}.

background radiation: the radiation detected by a radiation counter when no radioactive source is nearby.

▨ Background radiation detected in the laboratory is due mainly to cosmic radiation and natural radioactive sources in the ground. When measuring count-rate from a source, the background count-rate is deducted from the measured count-rate in order to obtain a more reliable measurement of the count-rate from the source (the corrected count rate).

bar: a non-SI unit of pressure equal to 0.1 MPa.

▨ Meteorologists frequently measure atmospheric pressure in millibars (mbar) because the atmospheric pressure varies about a value of 1000 mbar.

baryon: a particle composed of triplets of *quarks*.

▨ In AS/A-level physics, the best-known baryons are the *proton* and the *neutron*. Baryons together with *mesons* form the group of particles known as *hadrons*.

base quantity: one of the seven physical quantities of the *SI system* by which all other physical quantities are defined.

▨ The base quantities are *mass, length, time, temperature, amount of substance, electric current* and luminous intensity. (Luminous intensity has been included in the list for completeness; the quantity is not included in present AS/A-level specifications.) See *base unit* for the units of the base quantities.

base unit: one of the seven base units of the *SI system*, related to a *base quantity*, whose magnitude is defined without referring to any other units (apart from other base units).

Base quantity	Base unit in SI system	Symbol
Mass	Kilogram	kg
Length	Metre	m
Time	Second	s
Temperature	Kelvin	K
Amount of substance	Mole	mol
Electric current	Ampere	A
Luminous intensity	Candela	cd

β-decay: see *beta decay*.

becquerel, Bq: unit of measurement of activity of a radioactive source where 1 becquerel is equal to 1 disintegration per second.

■ *TIP* Activity in becquerel should not be confused with count rate or with frequency. The becquerel is concerned with the rate of disintegration of a source, whereas count rate measures the rate of detection of radiation by a detector and frequency is the number of oscillations made per unit time by a vibrating body:

- *activity* — disintegrations per second, unit becquerel (Bq)
- *count rate* — counts per second, unit per second (s^{-1})
- *frequency* — cycles per second, unit hertz (Hz) or per second (s^{-1})

beta decay: the spontaneous decay of a nucleus with the emission of a *beta particle*.

■ Since a beta particle is an electron ($_{-1}^{0}e$), the decay of nucleus X to nucleus Y may be represented by the nuclear equation

$$_{Z}^{A}X \longrightarrow {}_{Z+1}^{A}Y + {}_{-1}^{0}e + \text{energy}$$

Frequently, some of the energy released in the decay is seen as a gamma ray photon.

■ *TIP* It is the parent nucleus that is radioactive, not the beta particle.

beta particle: a particle which may be emitted from a radioactive nucleus.

■ A beta particle (β-particle) is a high-speed electron, travelling at speeds of up to $0.99\,c$. On passing through matter, beta particles lose energy by *ionisation*. The path length (penetration) of beta particles is several metres of air or a few millimetres of aluminium. A beta particle does not exist as a separate particle within the nucleus. In the process of radioactive decay of a nucleus, a neutron becomes a proton and an electron. The proton remains in the nucleus and the electron is ejected as a beta particle.

beta radiation: the outward movement of *beta particles* from a radioactive source.

■ The beta particles carry energy from the source and cause *ionisation* of the medium through which they travel.

bifilar suspension: a uniform beam, suspended horizontally by two threads of equal length.

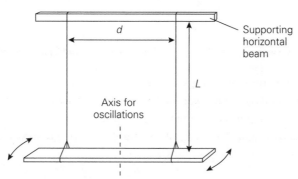

11

■ The beam is made to oscillate about a vertical axis through its centre. The period T of small oscillations about the central axis is related to the length L of the threads and their separation d by the expression

$Td \propto \sqrt{L}$

■ **TIP** Although the theory of the bifilar suspension is not in the AS/A-level specification (syllabus), it does provide a useful means of assessment of experimental techniques.

binding energy, nuclear: the work that would have to be done to separate a nucleus into its constituent *protons* and *neutrons*.

■ It may also be defined as the energy released if a nucleus is formed from its constituent protons and neutrons. This binding energy is seen as a mass defect. That is, the mass of the nucleus is less than the mass of the constituent particles. (See also *nuclear fission*; *nuclear fusion*; *binding energy per nucleon*.)

■ **TIP** Binding energies are frequently quoted in MeV, where

$1\,\text{MeV} = 1$ million *electronvolts* $= 1.6 \times 10^{-13}\,\text{J}$.

binding energy per nucleon: the *binding energy* of a nucleus divided by the number of *nucleons* in the nucleus.

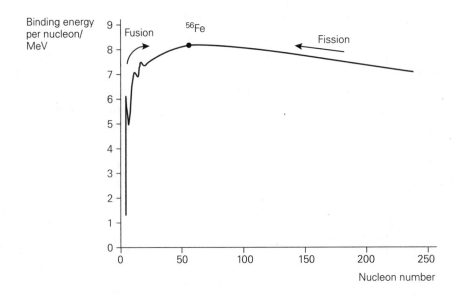

Variation of binding energy per nucleon with nucleon number

■ Since binding energy is energy released on formation of a nucleus, it follows that greater binding energy per nucleon leads to greater nuclear stability. Light nuclei can release energy during *nuclear fusion* and heavy nuclei release energy during *nuclear fission*. The peak of the graph, i.e. the greatest stability, is near iron-56.

blue shift: see *Doppler shift*.

boiling: the process whereby molecules of a substance in its liquid state enter the vapour state.

▨ Boiling occurs in the body of a liquid and at one temperature — the boiling point of the liquid. The boiling point is dependent on the external pressure acting on the liquid. Boiling occurs when the *saturated vapour pressure* is equal to the external pressure. In the process of boiling, bonds between molecules are broken and external work is done because the volume of a vapour is greater than the volume of the corresponding liquid. This requires energy. To maintain a constant temperature, thermal energy must be supplied to the liquid — this is the latent heat of vaporisation (see *specific latent heat*).

▨ *TIP* Note that the latent heat is referred to as 'latent heat of vaporisation' but boiling occurs under different circumstances from those for *evaporation*.

Boltzmann constant: the ratio of the *molar gas constant R* to the *Avogadro constant* N_A:

$$k = R/N_A = 1.38 \times 10^{-23} \, \text{J K}^{-1}$$

▨ The constant k relates the mean *kinetic energy* of a molecule of mass m of an *ideal gas* to its temperature T on the *thermodynamic scale of temperature*:

$$\text{mean kinetic energy} = \tfrac{1}{2}m<c^2> = \tfrac{3}{2}kT$$

The quantity $<c^2>$ is known as the *mean square speed* of the molecules.

Boyle's law: the pressure of a fixed mass of gas at constant volume is inversely proportional to its volume.

▨ For a mass of gas having pressure p_1 at volume V_1 and pressure p_2 at volume V_2, the temperature remaining constant, and since

$$p \propto 1/V \text{ and } pV = \text{constant}$$

we can say that

$$p_1V_1 = p_2V_2 = \text{constant}$$

The law was discovered by experiment and applies to all gases as long as they are at a sufficiently high temperature — the temperature being dependent on the gas itself. Boyle's law applies to oxygen and nitrogen at room temperature but not to carbon dioxide. (See also *ideal gas law*.)

▨ *TIP* Remember that the law applies to a fixed mass of gas at constant temperature.

β-particle: see *beta particle*.

β-radiation: see *beta radiation*.

breaking stress (also called 'strength', 'ultimate tensile stress'): the tensile *stress* at which a sample of material breaks.

▨ In non-scientific language, breaking stress is often referred to as the strength of the material.

bridge rectifier: an electrical component used for the conversion of an alternating current or voltage supply to a direct supply (see *rectification*).

b

brittle material: a material that shows no *plasticity* when subjected to a deforming force.

▪ The material does undergo *elastic deformation* but breaks without warning.

▪ *e.g.* This behaviour is typical of glasses, ceramics, concrete and cast iron.

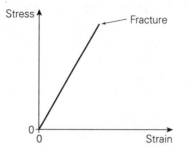

Stress–strain graph for a brittle material

brittleness: the property of *brittle materials*.

Brownian motion: the erratic *random motion* of small particles suspended in a fluid, providing evidence for the random nature of the motion of molecules in a liquid or a gas.

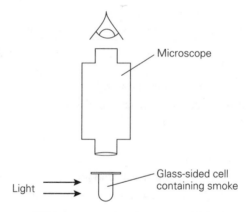

Demonstration of Brownian motion

▪ The particles must be small, such as pollen grains in water or smoke particles in air. Because of the random nature of the motion of molecules in the fluid, there are, at any moment of time, more molecules striking one face of the particle than another. This causes the particle to twist and turn. The motion of the particle is seen through the microscope as a speck of light moving erratically. Brownian motion provides some evidence for the postulates of the *kinetic theory of gases*.

▪ *TIP* It is the erratic motion of the particle, which is several thousand times larger than a molecule, that demonstrates the random motion of molecules in a fluid.

cantilever: a beam (e.g. a metre rule) clamped horizontally at one end with a load fixed to the other end, causing the end of the beam to be depressed.

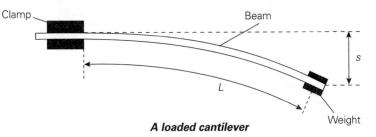

A loaded cantilever

■ The period T of small vertical oscillations of the mass is related to the distance L of the mass from the clamp by the expression

$$T^2 \propto L^3$$

The equilibrium depression s is given by

$$s \propto L^3$$

■ *TIP* Although the theory of the cantilever is not in the AS/A-level specification (syllabus), it does provide a useful means of assessment of experimental techniques.

capacitance: the ratio of the charge Q on a conductor to its potential V:

capacitance $C = Q/V$

■ The unit of capacitance is the farad (F), where

1 farad (F) = 1 coulomb per volt ($C\,V^{-1}$)

Capacitance is not relevant to an insulator because, when charge is placed on an insulator, there is no unique value for the potential. Capacitance applies to insulated *conductors* and to *capacitors*. In the case of a capacitor, a potential difference V is applied between the plates and charges of $+Q$ and $-Q$ are stored on the plates.

capacitor: a device for storing electric charge.

■ A capacitor usually has two conducting plates, separated by an insulator. A potential difference is applied between the plates, resulting in opposite charges being stored on the two plates. The symbol for an electrolytic capacitor indicates the polarity of the plates. The polarity of an electrolytic capacitor must be followed. The capacitance of a capacitor is measured in farads (F).

Electrolytic capacitor

The electrical symbol for a capacitor

capacitor discharge: the discharge of a charged capacitor through a resistor.

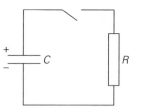

▓ Electrons, carrying negative charge, move from the negative plate of the capacitor of capacitance C through the resistor of resistance R and on to the positive plate of the capacitor. The variation with time t of the current I in the resistor and of the potential difference V across the resistor or across the capacitor is given by the expressions

$$I = I_0 e^{-t/RC}$$
$$V = V_0 e^{-t/RC}$$

where V_0 is the potential difference across the capacitor at time $t = 0$ and $I_0 = V_0/R$. The exponential variation with time t of the current I or the potential difference V is shown in the diagram below. (See also *time constant; smoothing.*)

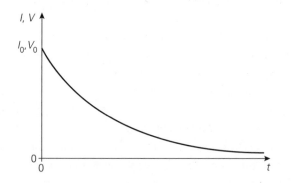

Variation of current or potential difference for a discharging capacitor

▓ **TIP** Since the charge on a capacitor is proportional to the potential difference between its plates, the charge Q is given by $Q = Q_0 e^{-t/RC}$.

capacitors in parallel: for capacitors of capacitance C_1, C_2 and C_3 connected in parallel, the combined capacitance C is given by

$$C = C_1 + C_2 + C_3$$

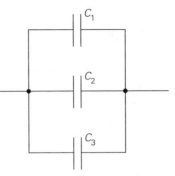

■ **TIP** The combined capacitance is larger than any individual capacitance.

capacitors in series: for capacitors of capacitance C_1, C_2 and C_3 connected in series, the combined capacitance C can be calculated from

$$1/C = 1/C_1 + 1/C_2 + 1/C_3$$

■ **TIP** The combined capacitance is smaller than any individual capacitance. Check your calculations to verify this, because many simple mistakes are made in the working.

Celsius scale of temperature: a scale of temperature based on the *thermodynamic scale of temperature.*

■ It is an arithmetical adjustment of the thermodynamic scale in which the zero is shifted. The Celsius temperature t, measured in degrees Celsius (°C), is related to Kelvin temperature T, measured in kelvin (K), by the expression

$$t/°C = T/K - 273.15$$

■ **TIP** In AS/A-level physics, data for calculations are frequently given to either two or three significant figures. The conversion $t/°C = T/K - 273$ is then appropriate, but you should remember the full conversion.

centi-: prefix used with a unit to denote the sub-multiple of $\times 10^{-2}$; its symbol is c.

■ **e.g.** 1 centimetre = $1 \times 10^{-2}\,\text{m}$ = 1 cm.

Centigrade scale of temperature: a scale of temperature based on the temperature of the freezing point and the boiling point of water and the variation with temperature of the property of a substance.

■ The scale relies on two fixed temperatures, or fixed points. The lower fixed point is the freezing point of water at *standard atmospheric pressure* and is taken as zero degrees Centigrade (0 °C). The temperature of vapour above water boiling at standard atmospheric pressure is taken as the upper fixed point, 100 °C. Temperatures other than at the fixed points are determined assuming that the property varies linearly with temperature. Such a scale is referred to as being an *empirical scale of temperature*.

centre of gravity (CG): the point at which the whole weight of a body may be thought to act.

■ The centre of gravity is the point about which an object will balance. If an object is thought to consist of very many small masses, the centre of gravity is the point about which the *moments* of the weights of all these small masses is zero. The position of the centre of gravity affects the *stability* of an object.

■ *e.g.* The centre of gravity of a uniform object is situated at its geometrical centre.

■ *TIP* Show the weight of an object as a single arrow pointing vertically downwards, with the arrow starting at the centre of gravity.

centre of mass: the point through which a single force must act for the object to accelerate linearly without any rotation.

■ In a uniform *gravitational field*, the centre of mass coincides with the *centre of gravity*.

centripetal acceleration: the acceleration, directed towards the centre of a circle, of an object moving along the arc of the circle (see also *centripetal force*).

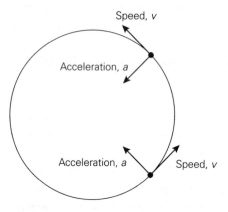

■ Although the linear speed of the object in the diagram is constant, its direction is changing continuously and hence its velocity is changing. The object must be accelerating. This acceleration is referred to as a centripetal acceleration because the change in velocity is always directed towards the centre of the circle. For an object with linear speed v travelling in a circular arc of radius r, the centripetal acceleration a is given by

$a = v^2/r$

Since *angular speed* ω is given by the expression $v = r\omega$

$a = v^2/r = r\omega^2$

■ *e.g.* Centripetal acceleration plays a part in geostationary orbits and in the motion of charged particles in a magnetic field.

centripetal force: the force, directed towards the centre of a circle, that is required for an object to travel along a circular path (see also *centripetal acceleration*).

■ An object of mass m has a constant speed v along the arc of a circle of radius r, as illustrated in the diagram. The centripetal force F is given by

$$F = mv^2/r = mr\omega^2$$

where ω is the angular speed of the object. Note that the centripetal force is obtained from the equation $F = ma$, where a is the centripetal acceleration. Also, since the speed v is constant, the kinetic energy of the object is constant. The centripetal force does no work on the object since this force is at right angles to its instantaneous velocity.

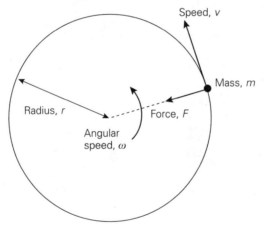

Speed, v

Mass, m

Radius, r

Force, F

Angular speed, ω

Circular motion

■ *e.g.* Force on a charged particle in a magnetic field and forces in geostationary orbits.

■ *TIP* The centripetal force is a resultant force towards the centre of the circle: the object is not in equilibrium.

CG: see *centre of gravity*.

chain reaction, nuclear: a series of similar reactions in which one of the products of a reaction causes further reactions to occur.

■ *e.g.* One important example is the fission of uranium-235

$$^{235}_{92}\text{U} + ^{1}_{0}\text{n} \longrightarrow ^{236}_{92}\text{U} \longrightarrow ^{140}_{54}\text{Xe} + ^{94}_{38}\text{Sr} + 2^{1}_{0}\text{n} + \gamma + \text{energy}$$

In this reaction, a *neutron* causes the fission of a uranium-235 nucleus, resulting in either two or three neutrons being emitted, dependent on the *isotopes* produced in the fission. These neutrons may cause further fissions. When the majority of the neutrons go on to cause further fissions, the chain reaction 'avalanches' and is said to be uncontrolled. In a nuclear reactor, some neutrons

C

are absorbed so that the chain reaction continues at a steady rate. The reaction is then said to be controlled.

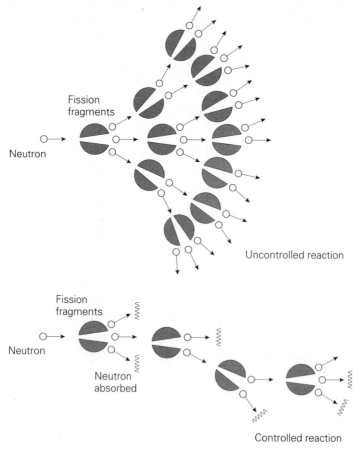

Chain reactions

charge carrier: a moving charged particle.

■ Since electric current is rate of flow of charge, the charge carriers constitute an electric current. In metals, the charge carriers are free electrons which move through the metal lattice. Charge carriers may be positively or negatively charged as in, for example, conduction in a solution of sodium chloride. (See also *conventional current; drift speed; Hall effect.*)

charged capacitor, energy of: the energy stored in a *capacitor* owing to the separation of the charges on its plates.

■ For a capacitor of *capacitance C* having a charge of magnitude Q on each of its plates and a potential difference V between them, the stored energy E is given by

$$E = \tfrac{1}{2}QV = \tfrac{1}{2}CV^2 = \tfrac{1}{2}Q^2/C$$

Energy is stored in the capacitor as a result of work done to transfer charge from one plate to the other. For any capacitor, the variation with charge Q of the potential difference V is as shown in the diagram below. Since energy $= v\Delta q$, the energy of the charged capacitor is represented by the area under the graph, i.e. energy $= \frac{1}{2}QV$.

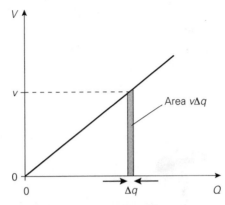

Variation with charge Q of the potential difference V across a capacitor

▨ **TIP** If you are asked to derive the formula $\frac{1}{2}QV$, be careful to indicate the area between the line on the graph and the Q-axis. Do not learn all of the formulae for energy. You must learn that capacitance $C = Q/V$. So, if you learn one of the formulae (better $E = \frac{1}{2}QV$ or $E = \frac{1}{2}CV^2$), then the substitution of $C = Q/V$ provides easy access to the other formulae.

charges, law of: a simple law to determine whether charges attract or repel, namely:
- like charges repel
- unlike charges attract

Charles's law: the volume of a fixed mass of gas at constant pressure is proportional to its temperature on the *thermodynamic temperature scale*.

▨ Since $V \propto T$ and $V/T =$ constant, if we take a fixed mass of gas having volume V_1 at thermodynamic temperature T_1 and volume V_2 at temperature T_2, with the pressure remaining constant, we can say that

$$V_1/T_1 = V_2/T_2 = \text{constant}$$

The law was discovered by experiment and applies to all gases as long as they are at a sufficiently high temperature — the temperature being dependent on the gas itself. Charles's law applies to oxygen and nitrogen at room temperature but not to carbon dioxide. The history of the experimental discovery is complicated by the development of temperature scales, as the original work was not done in terms of thermodynamic temperature. (See also *ideal gas law.*)

▨ **TIP** Remember that the law applies to a fixed mass of gas at constant pressure.

circular motion: the motion of an object following a circular path about a fixed point at constant speed.

■ For an object of mass m moving at constant speed v and angular speed ω in a circular path of radius r

linear speed $v = r\omega$

centripetal acceleration $a = v^2/r = r\omega^2$

centripetal force $F = mv^2/r = mr\omega^2$

cloud chamber: apparatus used to make visible the path of ionising radiation.

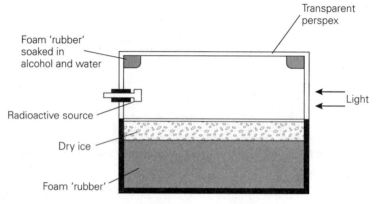

A simple cloud chamber

■ Air saturated with alcohol vapour is cooled by means of solid carbon dioxide (dry ice) so that the vapour becomes supersaturated. When ionising radiation passes through this vapour, it causes ionisation and the vapour condenses on the ions. The path of the ionising radiation is seen as a 'vapour trail'. The top of the chamber is rubbed to charge it by friction in order to remove stray ions. The cloud chamber is useful for the observation of *alpha particle* tracks since the density of ionisation is great and the tracks are dense. However, the ionisation produced by *beta particles* and *gamma radiation* is far less dense and, consequently, the tracks are difficult to see.

■ *TIP* Remember that we observe the droplets of condensed vapour, not the ionised air molecules.

coefficient of viscosity (also called just 'viscosity'): a measure of the viscous (drag) forces in a *fluid*.

■ Consider a layer of fluid (e.g. oil) of thickness Δx between two parallel glass sheets, each of area A.

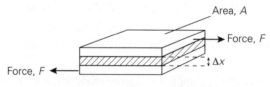

Defining coefficient of viscosity

The tangential force F required to maintain a constant difference in speed Δv between the glass sheets is given by the word equation

tangential force $\propto$ area $\times$ normal velocity gradient

$F = \eta A \, (\Delta v / \Delta x)$

The constant η is known as the coefficient of viscosity (viscosity) of the fluid and its SI unit is pascal second (Pa s). Note that the equation applies only to *streamline flow*. (See also *Stokes' law*; *Poiseuille's equation*.)

■ *TIP* The force is parallel to the area A and the velocity gradient ($\Delta v / \Delta x$) is measured at right angles to the area.

coherence: a term used to indicate that the *phase difference* between two waves remains constant and does not vary with time.

■ For two waves to be coherent, they must have the same frequency. Two *monochromatic* light sources have the same frequency but they do not emit coherent waves. Light consists of short pulses of waves (*photons*), and although the photons have the same frequency, they are emitted at random from the sources and consequently have no fixed phase difference between any two of them. Coherence and the overlapping of two waves are the conditions necessary for *interference* to occur. (See also *two-source interference*.)

collision: an interaction between two or more objects in which linear momentum is transferred from one object to another.

■ Contact between the objects is not necessary. Collisions may be either *elastic collisions* or *inelastic collisions*.

■ *e.g.* Collisions occur in alpha particle scattering and repulsion between magnets.

compression: a region in a medium where the pressure is above average.

■ Compressions are often associated with sound waves where a series of compressions and *rarefactions* move outwards from a sound source, carrying wave energy.

■ *e.g.* A *longitudinal wave* is made up of a series of compressions and rarefactions.

compressive forces: two forces acting on an object along a line in opposite directions so as to tend to reduce its length along the direction of the forces.

■ The forces do not cause any translational or rotational motion of the object. (See also *Young modulus*.)

■ *e.g.* The forces acting in the compression of a spring.

■ *TIP* Remember that two forces are involved, although we may only show one of them on a diagram. For example, in an experiment involving a coiled spring on a bench supporting a load, the load is, obviously, one of the two forces. The other force is supplied by the bench.

condensation: the process whereby molecules of a substance in its vapour state return to the liquid state.

■ Condensation can occur at any temperature so long as the temperature is such that the vapour is a *saturated vapour*. In the process of condensation, the latent heat of vaporisation is released as the bonds between molecules are formed (see *specific latent heat*). A scald with steam at 100 °C is far more serious than one with water at 100 °C because of the latent heat of vaporisation being released on condensation.

conductor, electrical: a material containing freely moving *charge carriers*.

■ Under the action of a small electric field, the charge carriers move through the conductor, constituting an electric current. (See also *resistance, electrical*; *resistivity*.)

■ *TIP* Do not confuse electrical conduction with thermal conduction. It is certainly unwise to refer to a 'conductor' unless it is clear which type is being discussed.

conservation of charge, law of: a fundamental law which states that electric charge cannot be created or destroyed.

■ There are two types of charge: 'positive' and 'negative'. Equal quantities of positive charge and negative charge result in an overall charge of zero. If, for example, a negative charge is created on a body, then an equal positive charge must be found somewhere else.

conservation of energy, law of: energy cannot be created or destroyed, but it can be converted (transferred) from one form to another.

Conservation of energy is a fundamental concept that applies to all branches of science. Many processes can be considered as conservation of energy or energy conversion (transfer). (See also *work*; *heating*; *first law of thermodynamics*; *mass–energy equivalence*.)

conservation of linear momentum, principle of: the total linear momentum of an isolated system in any given direction is constant.

■ The principle is a consequence of *Newton's third law of motion*.

■ *TIP* The system must be isolated: a rocket taking off from the Earth's surface is not an isolated system because the Earth exerts forces on the rocket. Such problems should be solved using the concept of the rate of change of momentum of the exhaust gases equalling the thrust.

constructive interference: the interference that occurs when two or more waves meet at a point such that the resultant displacement is greater than the largest individual displacement.

■ This is as a result of the *principle of superposition*. The waves must have the same frequency and transverse waves must be either unpolarised or polarised in the same plane (see *polarisation*). Complete constructive interference occurs when two waves are in *phase* (zero phase angle). The resultant amplitude is then the sum of the individual amplitudes. (See also *destructive interference*; *two-source interference*.)

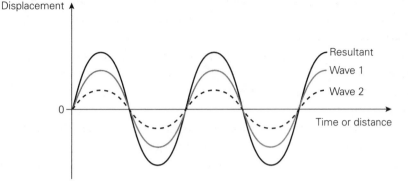

TIP Constructive interference can occur when there is a phase angle between the two waves. Only if the constructive interference is to be total do the two waves have to be in phase.

continuous spectrum: a distribution of emitted wavelengths of electromagnetic radiation produced by a body, with no breaks between its extreme values.

■ Continuous spectra are produced by hot solids and hot gases at high pressure.

■ **e.g.** Spectrum of white light.

control rod: a rod used in a *thermal fission reactor* to absorb neutrons and thus control the rate at which fission reactions continue.

■ Control rods are frequently made of boron steel. When the rods are lowered into the reactor core, the rate of reaction is slowed down.

conventional current: see *electric current*.

cooling: the lowering of the temperature of an object.

■ Frequently, what is measured is rate of cooling. This is the gradient of the graph when temperature is plotted against time. The unit is kelvin per second ($K s^{-1}$).

■ **TIP** Do not confuse rate of cooling with rate of loss of thermal energy (heat). When a liquid is freezing, its temperature remains constant. Therefore, although it will be losing thermal energy, its rate of cooling will be zero.

corkscrew rule, Maxwell's: a rule used for finding the direction of the magnetic field around a straight wire.

If you imagine screwing a right-handed corkscrew in the direction of the current, the direction of motion of your thumb gives the direction of the magnetic field. (See also *magnetic flux density due to a long straight wire*.)

cosmic radiation: radiation received on Earth from outer space; it consists of many different types of particles and also *electromagnetic radiation*.

■ Since cosmic radiation is a mixture of particles and electromagnetic waves, it is not considered to be part of the *electromagnetic spectrum*. Some of the *photon* energies are so great that they must be due to processes in stars.

■ **TIP** It used to be thought that cosmic radiation is part of the electromagnetic spectrum, and if you look at some old textbooks, you will see that it is included.

However, you should not include it as part of the electromagnetic spectrum because cosmic radiation includes high-energy particles.

coulomb, C: the SI unit of electric charge.

■ It is that charge flowing per second past a point in a circuit in which the current is 1 ampere:

charge in coulombs = (current in amps) × (time in seconds)

$$\Delta Q = I\Delta t$$

where ΔQ is the charge passing the point when a current I flows for time Δt.

Coulomb's law: the force between two point charges is proportional to the product of the charges and inversely proportional to the square of their separation.

■ The force F acting on point charges Q_1 and Q_2, separated by a distance r, is given by

$$F = kQ_1Q_2/r^2$$

where k is a constant. The constant k depends on the medium in which the charges are placed. For a vacuum

$$k = 1/4\pi\varepsilon_0$$

where ε_0 is the *permittivity of free space* ($8.85 \times 10^{-12}\,\mathrm{F\,m^{-1}}$). In general, the force is reduced by an intervening medium, that is, the constant k is smaller for a medium than for a vacuum. Using the value $1/4\pi\varepsilon_0$ for the constant k when the charges are in air introduces only a very small error and, at AS/A-level, this approximation is made with little or no comment.

■ *TIP* It is sometimes useful to remember that $1/4\pi\varepsilon_0 \approx 9 \times 10^9$, but be careful because this value is to one significant figure only and, where data for calculations are given to two or more significant figures, the approximation is inappropriate. Do not confuse this constant k with the *Boltzmann constant*, which is also denoted by the symbol k.

count rate: the rate at which emissions from a radioactive source are detected; it is measured in $\mathrm{s^{-1}}$ (per second).

■ Count rate is not the same as *activity*. This is illustrated by the fact that activity has the unit becquerel (Bq) where $1\,\mathrm{Bq} = 1\,\mathrm{s^{-1}}$. The rate at which nuclei disintegrate is the activity, but not all of the emissions will be counted. Some of the radiation will be absorbed in the source itself, and some between the source and the detector. Furthermore, not all of the radiation is directed towards the detector.

couple: two forces of equal magnitude but acting in opposite directions whose lines of action are parallel but separate.

■ A couple produces rotational motion but not translational motion. For two equal but opposite parallel forces, each of magnitude F, with their lines of action separated by a distance d, the magnitude of the turning effect of the couple (the *torque* of the couple) is given by

torque of couple = Fd

C

Torque is a *vector quantity* and the SI unit of torque is newton metre (N m).

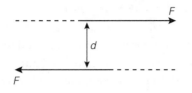

Two forces acting as a couple

■ **e.g.** The forces used to turn the handle of a screwdriver act as a couple.

■ **TIP** Do not confuse the unit of torque with that of energy (the joule). Both are the product of a force and a distance. In the case of torque, the force and distance are at right angles. For energy, the force and the distance moved are along the same line.

critical angle: when a ray of light in an optically more dense medium meets a boundary with an optically less dense medium and is partially reflected and partially refracted parallel to the boundary, the angle of incidence i is the critical angle C.

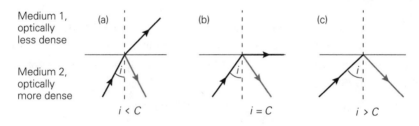

Critical angle and total internal reflection

■ For small angles of incidence, as in part (a) of the diagram, the ray is partly reflected and partly refracted away from the normal. For large angles of incidence, as in part (c), the ray undergoes *total internal reflection*. In part (b) the ray is partially reflected and any refracted ray travels parallel to the boundary. The angle of incidence in (b) is referred to as the critical angle C. For angles of incidence less than C, refraction and reflection occur. For angles of incidence greater than C, the ray is totally internally reflected. At the critical angle C, the angle of refraction is 90°. The *refractive index* $_2n_1$ for the ray on the boundary from medium 2 is given by

$$_2n_1 = \frac{\sin C}{\sin 90}$$

Hence

$$\sin C = {_2n_1}$$

and

$$_1n_2 = \frac{1}{\sin C}$$

C

■ *e.g.* For glass in air, the refractive index $_1n_2$ is about 1.5. Hence $C \approx 42°$. This fact is used in *reflecting prisms*. (See also *optic fibres*.)

■ *TIP* Remember that critical angle can be observed only when a ray in an optically more dense medium is incident on a boundary with an optically less dense medium. Also, critical angle and total internal reflection are not phenomena of light only. They are common to all waves.

critical damping: see *damping, degrees of.*

current: see *electric current.*

current–voltage characteristics (also called '*I/V* characteristics')**:** the variation with potential difference *V* of the current *I* in a circuit component.

 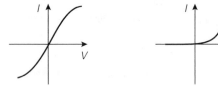

Metallic conductor   Filament lamp   Semiconductor diode
at constant temperature

■ *TIP* Always draw the characteristic for both negative and positive values of *V*. There may be surprises when reversing the potential difference (as for a diode)! The *resistance* is found using the co-ordinates of a single point, not the gradient of the graph line.

damped oscillations: oscillations in which the amplitude diminishes with time as a result of dissipative forces that reduce the total energy of the oscillations.

▨ A certain fraction of the total energy is lost during each oscillation. Consequently, the amplitude decreases exponentially with time. If the damping forces are large, oscillations may not occur. (See also *damping, degrees of.*)

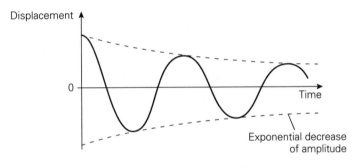

Lightly damped oscillations

▨ *e.g.* The function of a car's suspension is to reduce the total energy of oscillations.

▨ *TIP* When sketching a graph of damped oscillations, be careful to keep constant the period of oscillation. Start your sketch by marking off equal distances on the time axis for each half period. It is very tempting to reduce the period as the amplitude decreases!

damping, degrees of: the degree of damping determines the form of the decay of the amplitude of vibration of an oscillating body.

▨ Degree of damping is described in three categories:

• light damping — the object undergoes a number of complete oscillations with the amplitude of vibration decreasing exponentially with time. The greater the amount of damping, the greater the rate of decay of amplitude.

• critical damping — the displacement is reduced to zero in the minimum time possible without any oscillations occurring.

d

- heavy damping — the displacement reduces exponentially with time. There are no oscillations and the time for the displacement to decrease by a certain fraction is longer than for critical damping. This time increases as the degree of damping increases.

The three categories are illustrated below, together with undamped oscillations. (See also *damped oscillations*.)

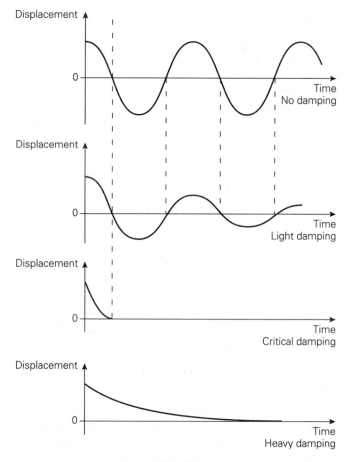

Damped oscillations

■ *TIP* Do not confuse damping with *resonance*. Damping is concerned with the dissipation of the energy of an oscillating body. On the other hand, resonance involves the imparting of energy to a body to maintain a maximum amplitude of vibration.

daughter nucleus: a product of a nuclear reaction.

■ In a nuclear reaction a *parent nucleus* is transformed with the emission of particles and/or energy into a daughter product:

parent nucleus → daughter nucleus

d

TIP The daughter nucleus may, itself, be transformed into a different daughter product.

de Broglie equation: an equation that relates the *momentum p* of a particle to its associated wavelength λ.

The equation is

$$\lambda = h/p$$

where h is the *Planck constant*. (See also *wave–particle duality*; *electron diffraction*.)

decay constant: see *radioactive decay constant*.

deceleration: a decrease in the velocity of a body.

It is said to be a negative *acceleration* where the positive direction is the direction of travel. An alternative name for deceleration is *retardation*.

degree Celsius, °C: the unit of temperature difference on the *Celsius scale of temperature*.

It is numerically equal to the *kelvin*, i.e. the fraction 1/273.16 of the difference in temperature between the *absolute zero of temperature* and the *triple point* of water.

degree Centigrade, °C: the unit of temperature difference on the *Centigrade scale of temperature*.

It is numerically equal to the fraction 1/100 of the difference in temperature between the freezing point of water at standard atmospheric pressure and the temperature of vapour above water boiling at standard atmospheric pressure.

TIP Remember that the degree Celsius and the degree Centigrade have the same magnitude. Celsius temperatures are used because they are related to the *thermodynamic scale of temperature* and are not empirical.

density: the mass per unit volume of a substance, defined by the word equation

$$\text{density} = \frac{\text{mass}}{\text{volume}}$$

For an object of mass M and volume V, its density ρ is given by

$$\rho = M/V$$

The SI unit of density is kilogram per metre cubed ($\text{kg}\,\text{m}^{-3}$).

e.g. The density of water is about $1000\,\text{kg}\,\text{m}^{-3}$; all solids and liquids have densities of this order of magnitude. In general, the density of gases is about 1000 times less than that of solids or liquids.

TIP When defining density, make sure that you indicate clearly that there is a ratio. A definition such as 'mass in a unit volume' is not satisfactory.

destructive interference: the interference that occurs when two or more waves meet at a point such that the resultant displacement is less than the largest individual displacement.

This is as a result of the *principle of superposition*. The waves must have the same frequency and be out of phase, and transverse waves must be either unpolarised or polarised in the same plane (see *polarisation*). Complete destructive inter-ference occurs when two waves have the same amplitude and are in *antiphase* (π rad phase angle). (See also *constructive interference; two-source interference*.)

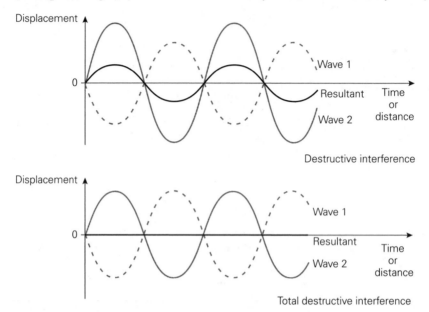

Destructive interference

Total destructive interference

■ *TIP* Destructive interference implies an overall reduction in amplitude. Only if total destructive interference occurs can the resultant amplitude be said to be zero.

diffraction: the spreading of waves at an edge or a slit so that the waves do not travel in straight lines.

▓ Diffraction is a phenomenon associated with waves and provides evidence for the wave nature of *electromagnetic radiation*. The extent of the bending depends on the relative sizes of the wavelength of the wave and the dimensions of the slit used to demonstrate the effect. The effect becomes more pronounced as the slit width approaches the wavelength. Diffraction effects may be demon-strated using a *ripple tank*.

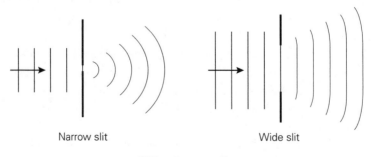

Narrow slit   Wide slit

Diffraction at a slit

Note that, if diffraction of light through a single slit is being demonstrated, the extent of the diffraction is small because, even with a narrow slit, the wavelength of the light is still hundreds of times smaller than the slit width. (See also *two-source interference*.)

■ *TIP* When drawing diagrams to illustrate diffraction, do make sure that the wavefronts remain equally spaced. There is no change in wavelength, only a change in direction, unlike the situation where *refraction* occurs.

diffraction grating: a small sheet of glass or transparent plastic on which have been marked many hundreds of parallel, equally spaced lines.

■ A typical grating will have about 1000 lines per centimetre, giving line spacings of only a few wavelengths of light. Parallel monochromatic light (possibly from a *laser*) is directed normally on to the grating. A series of bright, symmetrically spaced dots is observed on a screen placed some distance away from the grating. Corresponding pairs of bright dots are referred to as 'orders of diffracted light'.

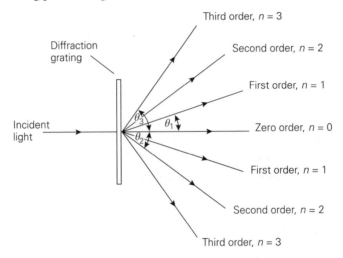

Use of a diffraction grating

The wavelength λ of the incident light may be determined, knowing the spacing d of neighbouring lines on the grating and the angle of diffraction θ of any order of diffracted light.

- For the first order, $\lambda = d \sin \theta_1$
- For the second order, $2\lambda = d \sin \theta_2$
- For the third order, $3\lambda = d \sin \theta_3$
- For the nth order, $n\lambda = d \sin \theta_n$

The spacing d of the lines (the *grating element*) may be determined from the number N of lines per unit length of the grating.

$\quad d = 1/N$

(See also *diffraction*.)

d

■ *TIP* If asked to find how many orders of diffracted light will be seen with a particular grating, substitute the value of the wavelength λ of the light into the formula $n\lambda = d\sin\theta$ and remember that $\sin\theta$ cannot be greater than 1. For gratings with a small grating element d, there may be only one or two orders of diffracted light.

diode: an electrical device that allows current through it in one direction only.

■ The 'ideal diode' has infinite resistance in one direction and a small finite resistance in the other. The variation of current I with applied voltage V is shown in the first diagram below. The circuit symbol for a diode is shown in the second diagram. The direction of conventional current when the diode conducts is shown by the arrowhead. When the diode is conducting, it is said to be forward biased. When it is not conducting, it is reverse biased.

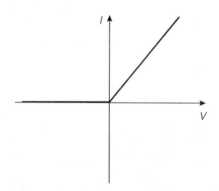

Current–voltage characteristic for an ideal diode

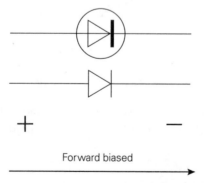

Forward biased

Circuit symbol for a diode

■ *e.g.* Diodes are used for the *rectification* of alternating voltages.

displacement: the distance of an object or a point, in a specified direction, from some reference point.

■ Displacement is a *vector* quantity and it defines the position of a point with reference to a fixed position.

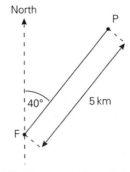

Displacement of a point

In the diagram, the displacement of P from F is 5 km at an angle of 40° east of north.

■ *e.g.* Displacement is used to define the position of a point undergoing *oscillations* and for defining what is meant by *transverse waves* or *longitudinal waves*.

■ *TIP* Do not confuse displacement with distance moved. An athlete running a 1000 m race completes four laps of the track. His distance moved is 1000 m but his displacement from the starting point is zero!

displacement–time graph: a graph showing the variation with time of the *displacement* of an object or a point.

■ Displacement is a vector quantity and, consequently, such graphs describe motion in one direction only (e.g. upwards and downwards, left and right). The gradient at a point on a displacement–time graph is a measure of the *velocity* of the object at that time.

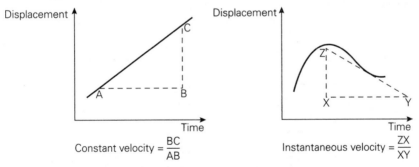

Calculation of velocity using displacement–time graphs

■ *TIP* A positive gradient is a velocity in the same direction as the displacement. A negative gradient means that the velocity is in the opposite direction to the displacement.

distance–time graph: a graph showing the variation with time of the distance travelled by an object.

■ Distance travelled cannot decrease, but only remain constant or increase. Thus the line of the graph can never show a decrease.

d

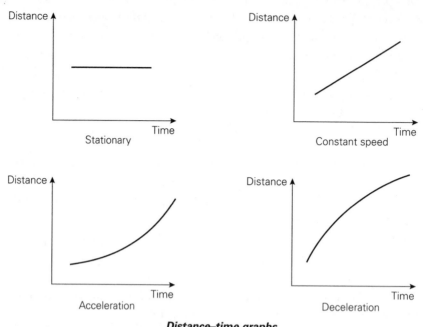

Distance–time graphs

Distance travelled is a scalar quantity. The gradient at a point on a distance–time graph gives the *speed* of the object at that time. An increasing or decreasing gradient indicates whether the object is accelerating or decelerating respectively.

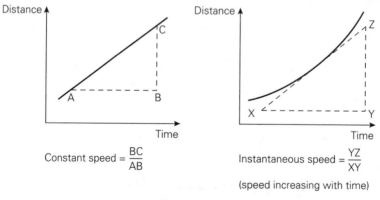

Calculation of speed

■ *TIP* Note that since distance travelled is scalar, the gradient of the graph gives only the magnitude of any acceleration along the direction in which the object is moving.

Doppler shift: the apparent change in frequency and wavelength of a wave when there is relative motion between the source of the waves and the observer.

■ For a wave of speed c, frequency f and wavelength λ, if the change in frequency and wavelength are Δf and $\Delta\lambda$ respectively, when the relative speed between source and observer is v, then

$$v/c = \Delta f/f = \Delta\lambda/\lambda$$

In astronomy, if the apparent wavelength is longer, the light is said to have been red shifted and the source is moving away from Earth. Blue shift indicates a source moving towards Earth.

drag forces: see *viscous forces.*

drift speed: the average speed at which *charge carriers* move through a conductor when there is an electric current in the conductor.

■ For a conductor carrying a current I at right angles to an area of cross-section A, the drift speed v is related to the current by the expression

$$I = nAqv$$

where n is the number of charge carriers per unit volume (the number density) and q is the charge on each carrier. (See also *Hall effect.*)

■ *e.g.* For copper, $n \approx 10^{29}\,\mathrm{m^{-3}}$, giving typical drift speeds of about $0.5\,\mathrm{mm\,s^{-1}}$. Drift speeds are much higher in *semiconductor* materials where n is lower.

■ *TIP* Although drift speed is low, a lamp will light almost immediately when the current is switched on. It should be remembered that the electric field (which makes the carriers move) travels through the wires at the speed of electromagnetic waves. Thus all carriers are made to drift along the wire at almost the same time.

ductile material: a material that is capable of having its shape changed permanently without breaking.

■ Once the material is plastic, a small increase in *stress* can cause a large increase in *strain*, resulting in a permanent change in shape.

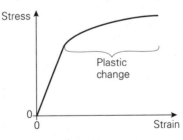

Stress–strain graph for a ductile material

■ *e.g.* Copper is a ductile material since it can be drawn out into thin wires.

efficiency: the ratio of the work got out of a *machine* to the energy put in:

$$\text{efficiency} = \frac{\text{work got out}}{\text{energy put in}}$$

■ Efficiency is often expressed as a percentage. In any machine there is bound to be some wastage of energy in, for example, overcoming frictional forces. As a result, in any practical machine, efficiency is less than 100%.

■ *e.g.* Efficiency is an important characteristic of a *heat engine*.

elastic collision: a collision between two or more objects in which *kinetic energy* is conserved.

■ That is, the total kinetic energy of the objects before the collision is equal to the total kinetic energy after the collision. No kinetic energy is converted (transferred) into any other form of energy. As in all types of collision, linear momentum is conserved. An alternative way in which an elastic collision between two objects may be defined is to say that the velocity of separation is equal to the velocity of approach.

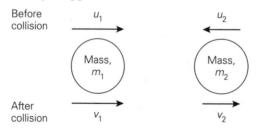

Head-on elastic collision

The elastic collision may be summarised as:

conservation of kinetic energy: $\frac{1}{2}m_1u_1^2 + \frac{1}{2}m_2u_2^2 = \frac{1}{2}m_1v_1^2 + \frac{1}{2}m_2v_2^2$

velocity of separation = velocity of approach: $v_2 - v_1 = u_1 + u_2$

conservation of linear momentum: $m_1u_1 - m_2u_2 = m_1v_1 + m_2v_2$

In practice, very few collisions are wholly elastic. A small fraction of the kinetic energy is converted into other forms. Nevertheless, calculations assuming elastic collisions may yield results which are a good approximation to the actual situations.

▨ *e.g.* Elastic collisions occur during alpha particle scattering and the *radioactive decay* of a nucleus.

▨ *TIP* Remember to state that kinetic energy is conserved; it is not sufficient to state that 'energy is conserved', because this is true in all situations!

elastic constant: see *spring constant.*

elastic deformation: a change in shape of a sample of material such that, when the distorting forces are removed, the sample returns to its original shape and size.

elasticity: the tendency of an object or a sample of material to return to its original shape and size when any deforming forces are removed from it.

▨ Elasticity is the opposite of *plasticity.* (See also *spring constant; Hooke's law.*)

elastic limit: the maximum *stress* which can be applied to an object such that, when the stress is removed, the object returns to its original shape and size.

▨ If the elastic limit is exceeded, the object will behave plastically, i.e. it will have a permanent change in shape when the stress is removed.

▨ *e.g.* The limit up to which *Hooke's law*, the *spring constant* and the *Young modulus* apply or have meaning.

electrical energy: energy associated with an *electric current.*

▨ For a source of electrical energy (e.g. a battery or a generator) of *electromotive force E* supplying current I, the energy converted into electrical form in time t is given by

$$\text{electrical energy} = EIt$$

Similarly, for a resistor of resistance R having a potential difference V across it when current I flows through it for time t, the electrical energy converted is given by

$$\text{electrical energy} = VIt$$

In the SI system, electrical energy is measured in joules (J). Since *electrical resistance R* is defined as $R = V/I$, electrical energy is given by

$$\text{energy} = (V^2/R)t = I^2Rt$$

▨ *e.g.* The *kilowatt-hour* is a commonly used practical unit of electrical energy.

▨ *TIP* Remember that energy = power × time. So long as you know the power, there is no need to find the current and voltage in order to calculate energy. You should learn the formulae energy = VIt and $R = V/I$. The other formulae for energy can then be derived quickly if you need them.

electrical power: either the rate of supply of electrical energy by a source or the rate of conversion (transfer) of electrical energy to other forms in an electrical component.

▨ For a source of electrical energy (e.g. a battery or a generator) of *electromotive force E* supplying *electric current I*

$$\text{electrical power } P = EI$$

If the electrical component has a *potential difference V* across it, then

electrical power $P = VI$

In the SI system, electrical power is measured in watts (W), where 1 watt is 1 joule per second ($J\,s^{-1}$). Since *electrical resistance R* is defined as $R = V/I$, power P is given by

$$P = V^2/R = I^2R$$

■ *TIP* You should learn the formulae $P = VI$ and $R = V/I$. The other formulae for power can then be derived quickly if you need them.

electric charge: for a constant *electric current I* in a circuit, the electric charge ΔQ passing one point in the circuit in an interval of time Δt is given by

$$\Delta Q = I\Delta t$$

■ Charge may be defined by the word equation

charge passing a point = current × time for which current flows

The SI unit of charge is the coulomb (C). There are two types of charge, and when equal quantities of these two types combine, the resultant charge is zero. Hence the types of charge are referred to as 'positive' and 'negative'. By convention, the charge on an *electron* is negative.

■ *TIP* Remember that the *base quantity* is electric current and that charge is defined in terms of current.

electric current: a flow of charged particles, which may be positively or negatively charged.

■ By convention, the current in an external circuit is from the positive terminal of the power source towards the negative terminal. The current is referred to as the conventional current and is a flow of positive charge. In a metallic conductor, charge is carried by *electrons* that are negatively charged. Electron flow is in the opposite direction to conventional current. Current is one of the *base quantities* in the SI system; it is measured in *amperes* (A).

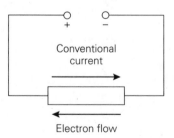

Conventional current and electron flow

electric field: a region of space where a force acts on a stationary charge.

■ The direction of the electric field is the direction of the force on a positive charge.

■ **TIP** The definition is in terms of the force on a stationary charge, although the force is unchanged regardless of speed. It should be remembered that a force on a moving charge could indicate that a *magnetic field* is present.

electric field lines: lines that show the direction of the force acting on a stationary positive point charge in the field.

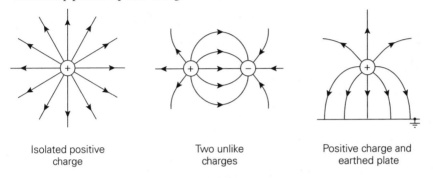

| Isolated positive charge | Two unlike charges | Positive charge and earthed plate |

Electric field patterns

■ Electric field lines do not touch or cross and are normal to any conducting surface. The pattern of the field for an isolated spherical conductor is of particular significance. From outside the sphere, all the lines appear to be diverging from its centre. The sphere acts as a point charge with the charge situated at its centre, i.e. a *radial field*.

electric field strength: the force per unit positive charge acting on a stationary charge placed at that point.

■ If a force F acts on a stationary positive charge Q, then the electric field strength E is given by

$$E = F/Q$$

The SI unit of electric field strength is, by definition, newton per coulomb ($N\,C^{-1}$). Electric field strength is equal to potential gradient and therefore its unit may be given as volt per metre ($V\,m^{-1}$). (See also *Millikan's oil drop experiment*.)

electric field strength of a point charge: given by the expression

$$E = Q/4\pi\varepsilon_0 r^2$$

where E is the electric field strength at a point distance r from a point charge Q and ε_0 is the *permittivity of free space*.

■ The expression is derived using *Coulomb's law*

$$F = Q_1 Q_2/4\pi\varepsilon_0 r^2$$

and remembering that electric field strength is force per unit charge (F/Q).

■ **TIP** The formula applies to a charged spherical conductor when the distance r is greater than the radius of the sphere.

electric potential: the electric potential at a point is the work done per unit positive charge in moving a point charge from infinity to the point.

■ The potential at infinity is defined as zero. Potentials may be positive or negative, depending on whether the potential is due to a positive or to a negative charge. Work must be done on a positive charge in moving it from infinity towards a fixed positive charge and thus the potential is positive. Work is done by a positive charge in moving it towards a negative charge, resulting in a negative potential. The electric potential V at a distance r from a point charge Q is given by

$$V = Q/4\pi\varepsilon_0 r$$

where ε_0 is the *permittivity of free space*. In the SI system, electric potential is measured in joules per coulomb ($J\,C^{-1}$) or volts (V). Note that, if the potential at a point is V, then the work done W in moving a charge Q from infinity to that point is

$$W = VQ$$

■ *TIP* The formula applies to a charged spherical conductor when the distance r is greater than the radius of the sphere.

electric potential difference: the electric potential difference between two points is the work done per unit charge in moving a small positive charge between the two points.

■ It is sometimes loosely called 'voltage'. Potential difference is defined by the word equation

$$\text{potential difference } V = \frac{\text{work done } W}{\text{charge transferred } Q}$$

The equation may be re-written as

$$\text{potential difference } V = \frac{W}{\Delta t} \times \frac{\Delta t}{Q}$$

where Δt is the time during which the charge is transferred. Referring to the definitions of *electrical power P* and *electric current I*

$$\text{potential difference } V = P/I$$

The SI unit of potential difference is the *volt* (V). It may also be given as the watt per amp ($W\,A^{-1}$).

■ *TIP* The work done is a transfer of electrical energy to some other form, e.g. thermal energy in a resistor. This fact is important when distinguishing a potential difference from an *electromotive force*, where some form of energy is transferred into electrical energy.

electromagnet: a device which behaves as a magnet only when an electric current passes through its coils.

■ The current in a coil of insulated wire wrapped around a *soft iron* core causes the core to be magnetised. When the current is switched off, the soft iron loses its magnetism. As well as behaving as a temporary magnet, the soft iron increases the strength of the magnetic field by up to 1000 times.

e

electromagnetic induction: the setting up, or inducing, of an *electromotive force* (emf) in a conductor whenever there is a change of *magnetic flux linkage*.

■ The magnetic flux linkage may be changed either by changing the magnitude of the magnetic flux or by moving a conductor or coil relative to a magnetic field. An emf is always induced when there is a change in (magnetic) flux linkage. If the coil forms part of a continuous circuit, then there will be an induced current. (See also *electromagnetic induction, laws of.*)

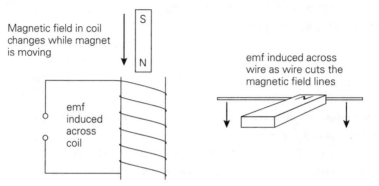

Changing the magnetic flux linkage

■ *TIP* When defining electromagnetic induction, always refer to induced emf. There may not be an induced current although there is a change in flux linkage.

electromagnetic induction, laws of: the two laws of electromagnetic induction are Faraday's law, which gives the magnitude of the *induced emf*, and Lenz's law, which gives the direction.

■ Faraday's law states that the emf induced in a conductor is proportional to the rate of change of *magnetic flux linkage*. If the magnetic flux linkage $N\phi$ is measured in weber-turns and the emf E in volts, then the constant of proportionality is unity and the mathematical relation for Faraday's law is

$$E = -\mathrm{d}(N\phi)/\mathrm{d}t$$

The negative sign is involved with the direction of the emf and is explained as part of Lenz's law.

■ Lenz's law states that the direction of the induced emf is such that it produces effects to oppose the change causing it. This law is a consequence of the law of *conservation of energy*. An emf is a source of electrical energy and that energy must have come from somewhere. The emf produces effects (e.g. a magnetic field due to the induced current) which oppose the change (e.g. this magnetic field due to the induced current opposes the change in the magnetic flux giving rise to it). Consequently, work has to be done to overcome this opposition and energy is conserved.

■ Since the induced emf produces effects to oppose the change in flux linkage, there must be a negative sign in the formula for Faraday's law to indicate opposite directions. An alternative way by which the direction of the induced emf in a conductor may be found is *Fleming's right-hand rule*.

▓ *TIP* When stating Faraday's law, always refer to the induced emf. There will always be an induced emf when there is a change in flux linkage but the current will be zero if the circuit is not complete. Many students state, for Lenz's law, that the emf opposes the change in flux linkage. This must be untrue — how can an emf oppose motion, for example? It is important that you state that the emf produces effects that oppose…

electromagnetic radiation: that group of waves which make up the *electromagnetic spectrum.*

▓ The waves are *transverse waves* and consist of oscillating electric and magnetic fields (vectors). All electromagnetic waves travel with the same speed in a vacuum ($3.00 \times 10^8 \, \mathrm{m\,s^{-1}}$).

electromagnetic spectrum: the range of *electromagnetic waves* listed according to their origins and properties.

▓ The spectrum is usually given in order of decreasing wavelength. All types of electromagnetic wave travel at the same speed ($3.00 \times 10^8 \, \mathrm{m\,s^{-1}}$) in a vacuum.

Name	Wavelength	Origin	Detection	Properties	Uses
Radio waves	>10 cm	Oscillating electrons	Radio aerials	Reflected by ionosphere, easily diffracted	Communications, radioastronomy
Microwaves	10 cm to 1 mm	Magnetrons	Tuned cavities	Reflected by metals, absorbed by water	Communications, cooking
Infrared (IR)	1 mm to 700 nm	Hot bodies	Photography, heating effect	Emitted by all bodies above 0 K, penetrates fog	Satellite surveying, TV controls
Visible	700 nm to 400 nm	Hot bodies, electron de-excitation	Eye, photography	Colour	Sight, communication
Ultraviolet (UV)	400 nm to 1 nm	Mercury lamps, electron de-excitation	Photography, fluorescence, solid-state detectors	Causes skin cancers, absorbed in upper atmosphere	Food sterilisation, atomic structure
X-rays	1 nm to 1 pm	X-ray tube, de-excitation of inner electrons	Photography, fluorescence	High penetration, health hazard	Diagnosis, radiotherapy, astronomy
Gamma rays (γ-rays)	1 pm to 1 fm	Nuclear decay	Photography, GM counter, scintillation counter	Very highly penetrating, health hazard	Diagnosis, radiotherapy

■ **TIP** In practice, there is no real division between parts of the spectrum and the regions are not all of the same size. Visible light occupies a very small part of the complete spectrum. Cosmic radiation is a mixture of particles and electromagnetic radiation, originating in outer space. Cosmic radiation should not be included as a region of the electromagnetic spectrum.

electromagnetic waves: waves consisting of oscillating electric and magnetic fields (*vectors*) that are at right angles to each other and to the direction of movement of the wave energy.

■ Electromagnetic waves are *transverse waves*. They are classified into different groups, dependent on their origin and properties, giving rise to the *electromagnetic spectrum*. The energy of electromagnetic waves is transported in discrete packets known as *photons,* where the energy of each photon is proportional to the frequency of the radiation. Increased *intensity* is seen as an increase in the number of photons per unit time per unit area. All electromagnetic waves travel at the same speed in a vacuum ($3.00 \times 10^8 \, \text{m s}^{-1}$).

electromotive force (emf): the energy transferred per unit charge from some form into electrical energy when charge is moved round a complete circuit:

emf = (energy transferred)/charge

■ The SI unit of emf is joule per coulomb (J C^{-1}) or volt (V). The emf of a supply may be determined by measuring the *potential difference* between the terminals of the supply when the supply is not delivering any current (open circuit).

■ **e.g.** A battery with an emf of 1.5 V converts 1.5 J of chemical energy to electrical energy when 1 C of charge is transferred around the complete circuit.

■ **TIP** Remember that the energy transfer is to electrical from some other form. This is important when distinguishing between emf and potential difference. Despite its name, do not be tempted to define emf as a force. An emf does not push charge around a circuit.

electron: a member of the group of fundamental particles known as leptons.

■ The electron has a charge of $-1.6 \times 10^{-19} \, \text{C}$ and a mass (when at rest) of $9.11 \times 10^{-31} \, \text{kg}$. Electrons are found in orbitals around the nucleus of an atom. (See also *electron diffraction; thermionic effect; photoelectric effect; emission spectrum.*)

electron diffraction: a technique used to investigate the spacing of crystal planes and the structure of surface films.

■ Electrons have a wavelength associated with them that is dependent on their momentum and is given by the *de Broglie equation*. Consequently, a beam of electrons is diffracted as it passes through a crystalline material in very much the same way as is an X-ray beam. The effect may be demonstrated in the laboratory. A narrow beam of electrons is directed at a thin gold foil or carbon film. A detecting screen beyond the film shows a series of concentric rings similar to that obtained when a laser beam is passed through a glass sheet covered with a fine powder. (See also *X-ray diffraction*; *neutron diffraction*.)

electron scattering, high-energy: a technique used to investigate the nuclei of atoms.

■ Very-high-energy electrons (energies of the order of GeV) are scattered by the nuclei of atoms since the associated de Broglie wavelength (given by the *de Broglie equation*) will be very short. The degree of scattering may be used to determine the radius and composition of nuclei.

electronvolt, eV: a non-SI unit of energy equal to the energy gained by an electron when it is accelerated through a potential difference of 1 volt.

■ Since electrical energy = charge × potential difference and the *elementary charge* is 1.6×10^{-19} C (see *Millikan's oil drop experiment*),

$$1\,eV = 1.6 \times 10^{-19}\,J$$

The electronvolt is used in atomic physics because the binding energies of electrons are of the order of a few eV. Furthermore, nuclear binding energies are of the order of MeV, where 1 MeV (mega-electronvolt) is 1.6×10^{-13} J.

■ *TIP* The numerical value of the electronvolt, in joules, is equal to the numerical value of the elementary charge in coulombs.

elementary charge: the smallest quantity of charge which can exist separately.

■ This implies that charge is quantised. The value of the elementary charge e is 1.602×10^{-19} C. The charge on an electron is -1.602×10^{-19} C and that on a proton is $+1.602 \times 10^{-19}$ C. (See *Millikan's oil drop experiment*.)

emf: see *electromotive force*.

emission spectrum, line: a series of separate, differently coloured lines on a black background corresponding to the wavelengths of electromagnetic radiation emitted by atoms when excited electrons in the atoms return to their ground states.

■ The lines are the coloured images of the slit at the front of the instrument used to split the light into its separate wavelengths. When an excited electron returns from an energy level E_2 to a lower one of energy E_1, a *photon* is emitted. The photon of radiation has frequency f and wavelength λ given by

$$(E_2 - E_1) = hf = hc/\lambda$$

where h is the *Planck constant* and c is the speed of light. Note that line spectra are produced by gases at low pressure where the atoms are well separated. For gases at high pressure, the atoms interfere with each other, causing their energy levels to change. Thus the sun and hot solids produce a *continuous spectrum*.

empirical scale of temperature: a scale of temperature that is based on the variation with temperature of a property of a substance, assuming that the property varies linearly with temperature.

■ Any property which varies with temperature may be used, e.g. volume of a liquid, pressure of a gas, electrical resistance. If a thermometer uses the property X of a substance which has a value X_0 at 0 °C, a value X_{100} at 100 °C and a value X_t at t °C, then the temperature t on the empirical Centigrade scale of that thermometer is given by

$$t = (X_t - X_0)/(X_{100} - X_0) \times 100\,°C$$

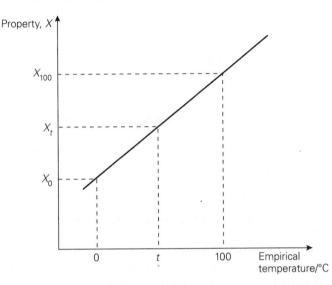

Since no property varies linearly with thermodynamic temperature, empirical temperatures on different thermometers only agree at the fixed points (0 °C and 100 °C).

■ **e.g.** The *thermistor thermometer*, the *thermocouple thermometer* and the *liquid-in-glass thermometer* all give temperature values on empirical scales.

energy: the stored ability to do *work*.

■ There are many different forms of energy; work is done when energy changes from one form to another. Energy has the same SI unit as that of work — the joule (J) — and is a *scalar quantity*.

■ **e.g.** *Kinetic energy, gravitational potential energy, electrical energy.*

energy level: the amount of energy of an extra-nuclear *electron*, above that of an electron in the *ground state*, possessed by the electron while it is in an orbital about the nucleus of an atom.

■ When an atom absorbs energy and, as a result, an electron moves from a lower energy level to a higher level, it is said to be in an *excited state*. The energy levels within a hydrogen atom are illustrated in the diagram. Note that the energy levels are shown as being negative. That is, energy must be provided in order for an electron to move to a higher, or excited, state. (See also *emission spectrum*; *absorption spectrum*; *ionisation*.)

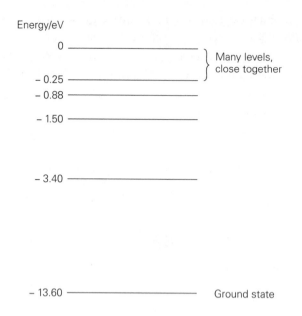

Energy levels within a hydrogen atom

■ *TIP* It is important to realise that the energy levels within an atom have specific values and that electrons cannot have energies between these values.

equations of motion: equations which relate change in displacement (distance moved) *s*, time taken *t*, initial velocity *u*, final velocity *v* and uniform acceleration *a*.

■ The equations may be derived from the defining equations for average *velocity* and for uniform *acceleration*. The equations are

$$v = u + at$$
$$s = ut + \tfrac{1}{2}at^2$$
$$v^2 = u^2 + 2as$$

These equations apply to uniformly accelerated motion. It is assumed that *s* = 0 when *t* = 0.

■ *TIP* Note that, in each of the equations, one of the variables *u*, *v*, *s* or *t* is not included. When solving problems involving these equations, it is often helpful to list the variables that are known. You should then choose an equation with only one unknown variable. Remember that the equations apply to uniformly accelerated motion — do not try to use them for *simple harmonic motion*!

equilibrium: an object which remains at rest or moving with a constant velocity under the action of a number of forces is said to be in equilibrium.

■ The conditions necessary for an object to be in equilibrium are:
  • the algebraic sum of the *forces* acting on the object in any direction must be zero

- the algebraic sum of the *moments* of the forces about any point in the object must be zero

Note that, when finding a sum, both force and moment of a force are vector quantities. There are three types of equilibrium:

- stable — the *centre of gravity* rises when the object is displaced slightly from its equilibrium position
- unstable — the centre of gravity falls when the object is displaced slightly from its equilibrium position
- neutral — the centre of gravity remains at the same height when the object is displaced from its equilibrium position

The different types of equilibrium may be illustrated using a ball, a spherical bowl and a flat surface. The curvature of the surface (concave, convex or flat) determines the motion of the ball when it is displaced slightly.

Stable   Unstable   Neutral

Different types of equilibrium

> **TIP** Remember that there are two conditions for an object to be in equilibrium. Students frequently quote only one of the two conditions, usually failing to consider moments of forces.

error: the difference between a measured quantity and its true value.

> If the true value is not known, then it is more correct to refer to an *uncertainty*. In some texts, the term 'probable error' is used as an alternative to uncertainty. (See also *precision*.)

> **TIP** An error is either above or below the true value, that is, it is either positive or it is negative. The symbol ± is used with an uncertainty because the doubt is in both directions.

evaporation: the process whereby molecules of a substance in its liquid state leave the surface of the liquid to enter the vapour or gaseous state.

> Evaporation can occur at any temperature at which liquid is present. In the process of evaporation, bonds between molecules are broken and external work is done because the volume of a vapour is greater than the volume of the corresponding liquid. This requires energy. If energy is not supplied to the liquid, its temperature will fall — cooling by evaporation. This is the principle of the refrigerator. To maintain a constant temperature, thermal energy must be supplied to the liquid — this is the latent heat of vaporisation (see *specific latent heat*).

excited state: when the energy of an extra-nuclear *electron* within an atom is greater than the minimum, the electron is said to be in an excited state.

■ Energy has been absorbed by the atom (e.g. as a result of heating) and some of this energy has been transferred to an electron so that it moves to a higher *energy level*. (See also *emission spectrum; absorption spectrum*.)

exponential change: a change such that the rate of growth or the rate of decay of a quantity is proportional to the amount of the quantity at that time.

■ For an amount y of a quantity, the rate of increase of the quantity is given by dy/dt. Thus, for an exponential increase of y with time t

$$dy/dt = ky$$

where k is a constant. This equation represents an *exponential growth*. If the quantity y decreases with time, then dy/dt is negative and

$$dy/dt = -ky$$

where k is a constant. This equation represents an *exponential decay*.

exponential decay: a change such that the rate of decay of a quantity is proportional to the amount of the quantity at that time.

■ The calculus form of the equation representing exponential decay is $-dy/dt = ky$ and the solution of this equation is

$$y = y_0 e^{-kt}$$

where y_0 is the value of quantity y at time $t = 0$. The solution is illustrated in the diagram below. One very significant feature of an exponential decay is that, no matter what the starting value of y, the time taken to halve the value of y is constant. This is also illustrated in the diagram.

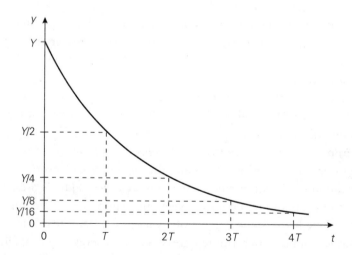

■ *e.g. Radioactive decay, half-life* and *capacitor discharge* are all examples of exponential decay.

■ *TIP* Exponential changes do not always involve time. The absorption of gamma radiation in matter follows an equation of the form

$$I = I_0 e^{-kx}$$

where I_0 is the *intensity I* of radiation for thickness $x = 0$ of absorber. The beam of gamma radiation is said to undergo *attenuation*. In some texts, the exponential function is written as 'exp'. Thus, $y = y_0e^{-kt}$ would be shown as $y = y_0\exp(-kt)$.

exponential growth: a change such that the rate of growth of a quantity is proportional to the amount of the quantity at that time.

■ The calculus form of the equation representing exponential growth is

$$dy/dt = ky$$

and the solution of this equation is

$$y = y_0e^{kt}$$

where y_0 is the value of quantity y at time $t = 0$. In theory, the growth of the quantity will increase indefinitely. In practice, some event will occur to prevent further growth. For example, exponential growth of amplitude of vibration of an object will, inevitably, lead to the destruction of the object.

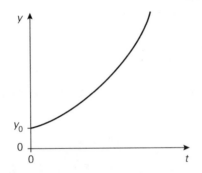

A second form of exponential growth involves an increase to a constant value. The mathematical expression for such a growth is

$$y = y_0(1 - e^{-kt})$$

where y_0 is the value of y at time $t = \infty$.

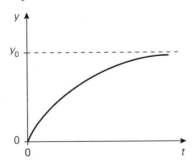

■ *e.g.* Charging a capacitor, time constant.

■ *TIP* In some texts, the exponential function is written as 'exp'. Thus, $y = y_0e^{kt}$ would be shown as $y = y_0\exp(kt)$.

extension: the increase in length of an object as a result of, for example, applying *tensile forces* to the object or heating it.

■ A decrease in length (a compression) is denoted as a negative extension. That is, if an extension is shown as Δl, the corresponding compression would be $-\Delta l$. (See also *spring constant; Hooke's law.*)

■ *TIP* The symbol Δ is used to represent 'change in...' Thus, Δl means 'change in l'.

Do not confuse extension with extended length:

extended length = original length + extension

farad, F: the SI unit of *capacitance* equal to one coulomb per volt.

■ The farad is a large unit and, in practice, capacitance of capacitors is generally measured in microfarads (μF) or picofarads (pF).

$$1\,\mu F = 10^{-6}\,F$$
$$1\,pF = 10^{-12}\,F$$

Faraday's law of electromagnetic induction: see *electromagnetic induction, laws of.*

femto-: prefix used with a unit to denote the sub-multiple of $\times 10^{-15}$; its symbol is f.

■ *e.g.* 1 femtometre = $1 \times 10^{-15}\,m$ = 1 fm. Nuclear diameters may be quoted in femtometres.

field: see *force-field.*

field of force: see *force-field.*

first law of thermodynamics: a statement of the law of *conservation of energy;* that is, for any system

$$\begin{array}{c}\text{increase in}\\ \textit{internal energy}\end{array} = \begin{array}{c}\text{thermal energy}\\ \text{supplied}\end{array} + \begin{array}{c}\text{external work done}\\ \text{on the system}\end{array}$$

■ The three quantities, as they are specified above, are all positive. If thermal energy is removed from the system, that quantity is negative. Similarly, if external work is done by the system, that quantity is negative in the equation. Note that there are different ways of expressing the law, depending on the direction of each energy transfer. The important point is to ensure that, when stating the law, the correct directions of energy transfer for all three quantities are made clear.

■ *e.g.* You should be familiar with the application of the law to an *adiabatic change*, an *isothermal change* and *evaporation*.

fission, nuclear: see *nuclear fission.*

Fleming's left-hand rule: a technique used to predict the direction of the force on a current-carrying wire or on a moving charged particle in a magnetic field.

■ Hold the first two fingers and thumb of your left hand at right angles to one another. When the *first* finger points in the direction of the magnetic *field* and the *se*cond finger points in the direction of the *c*urrent, then the thu*m*b gives the direction of the force (or *m*otion) on the conductor or on the charged particle.

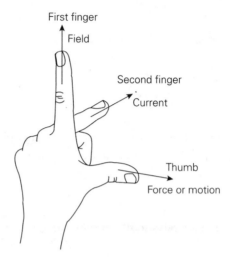

■ *TIP* Remember that the current direction is the direction of conventional current, i.e. the direction of movement of positive charge.

Fleming's right-hand rule: a technique used to determine the direction of the induced emf in a conductor moving through a magnetic field.

■ Hold the first two fingers and thumb of your right hand at right angles to one another. When the *first* finger points in the direction of the magnetic *field* and the thu*m*b points in the direction of *m*otion, then the *se*cond finger gives the direction of the induced emf or *c*urrent.

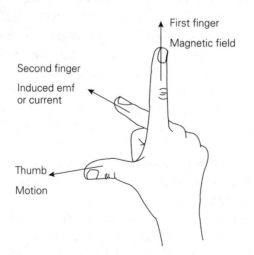

■ *TIP* A current is induced only if there is a complete circuit. An emf is always induced when there is a change in flux linkage.

flotation, principle of: an object floats in a fluid when it displaces a weight of fluid equal to its own weight.

■ The principle is an outcome of *Archimedes' principle*. There is an *upthrust* acting on the object and, when the object floats, this upthrust is equal to the weight of the object. Its *apparent weight* is then zero.

fluid: either a liquid or a gas but not a solid.

■ In a fluid, there are forces between molecules but these forces are not rigid. The molecules are free to move about within the body of the fluid, unlike in a solid, where atoms/molecules are held in fixed positions in a rigid structure. A consequence of this is that solids will transmit forces whereas liquids transmit pressures.

■ *TIP* In everyday language, we use the word 'fluid' to mean a liquid (hydraulic fluid, fluid balance in the body); you need to remember that gases are also fluids.

fluid pressure: see *pressure in a fluid*.

fluorescence: the emission of visible light from certain substances when *electromagnetic waves* of shorter wavelength are incident on them.

■ Fluorescence is one means by which *ultraviolet radiation* is detected. Ultraviolet light incident on fluorescene produces yellow-green light, on quinine sulphate it produces blue light and on chlorophyll, red light. Fluorescence may be produced when particles are incident on the substance. For example, high energy electrons colliding with a screen covered with zinc sulphide causes green light to be emitted.

■ *e.g.* The effect is used in television tubes and cathode-ray oscilloscopes.

flux linkage: see *magnetic flux linkage*.

focal length: see *principal focus*.

focal point: see *principal focus*.

force: a *vector quantity* that may change the shape of an object or, if the object is free to move, cause an *acceleration*.

■ Force is defined as the rate of change of *momentum* of an object which is free to move. For a change in momentum Δp occurring in time Δt, the force F acting in the direction of the change in momentum is given by

$$F = \Delta p / \Delta t$$

If the body has constant mass m, then

$$\Delta p = m\Delta v$$

where Δv is the change in velocity. Thus

$$F = m(\Delta v / \Delta t)$$

By definition, acceleration $a = \Delta v / \Delta t$ and hence, for a body of constant mass,

$$F = ma$$

As force is a vector quantity, the arrow representing force should always be shown starting at the point where the force is being applied. The SI unit of force is the *newton* (N).

▨ *TIP* Remember that force is defined by reference to momentum change. The equation $F = ma$ is not the defining equation for force because this equation is a special case of the more general equation $F = \Delta p/\Delta t$.

forced frequency of vibration (also called 'impressed frequency'): the frequency at which a body is made to vibrate by imposing a periodic force on it.

▨ *e.g. Resonance* occurs when the *natural frequency of vibration* of an object is equal to the forced frequency.

force-field (also called 'field', 'field of force'): a region of space that can be mapped with lines of force or with lines of potential.

▨ For AS/A-level physics, the fields which are studied are *electric fields, gravitational fields* and *magnetic fields.*

▨ *TIP* Lines of force in a field are usually plotted in a two-dimensional plane. Remember that, in practice, fields occupy a region of space and are three-dimensional.

freezing: the change in state of a substance from liquid to solid without any change in temperature.

The freezing process involves the release of thermal energy by the substance as rigid attractive bonds between atoms and molecules are formed.

TIP Freezing should not be confused with fusion; fusion (melting) is, in fact, the reverse of freezing.

frequency: in vibration, the number of oscillations made per unit time.

▨ The SI unit of frequency is the *hertz* (Hz), which is equal to one oscillation (or cycle) per second.

$$1\,\text{Hz} = 1\,\text{s}^{-1}$$

Frequency (in hertz) is related to *period* of oscillation T (in seconds) by the expression

$$f = 1/T$$

When carrying out calculations involving *simple harmonic motion*, the term *angular frequency* may be used. Angular frequency ω is related to frequency f (in Hz) by the expression

$$\omega = 2\pi f$$

where ω is measured in radians per second ($\text{rad}\,\text{s}^{-1}$).

▨ *e.g.* The pitch of a sound is related to the frequency of a wave. The UK mains electricity supply is delivered at a frequency of about 50 Hz.

▨ *TIP* Do not define frequency as the 'number of oscillations in unit time'. The ratio must be clear, i.e. 'number of oscillations per unit time'. Do not confuse the unit of activity or of count rate with that of frequency. All have the SI unit s^{-1}. However, activity and count rate are 'counts per second' and therefore the unit hertz (oscillations per second) is inappropriate.

fuel: the name given to any substance that provides a store of useful energy.

e.g. Petrol is a fuel in that it contains chemical energy that can be transformed into kinetic energy in a car engine.

TIP Do not confuse fuel and energy. A fuel is a form of energy.

fuel rod: a hollow metal alloy tube, sealed at both ends, containing the fuel (e.g. uranium-235) for a thermal fission reactor.

full-wave rectification: see *rectification*.

fusion: the process of melting whereby a substance changes state from solid to liquid without any change in temperature.

Thermal energy (latent heat) must be supplied to break some of the rigid attractive bonds between atoms and molecules (see *specific latent heat*).

TIP Fusion, or melting, is not to be confused with *nuclear fusion*, in which two light nuclei combine to form one heavier nucleus with the release of energy.

fusion, nuclear: see *nuclear fusion*.

gamma decay: the spontaneous decay of a nucleus with the emission of *gamma radiation.*

■ The gamma decay of a nucleus frequently accompanies *alpha decay* or *beta decay.* Alpha or beta decay usually leaves the *daughter nucleus* in an excited state. The daughter nucleus emits energy in the form of a gamma ray *photon* in order to reach its ground state.

■ *TIP* It is the parent nucleus that is radioactive, not the emitted particles.

gamma radiation: *electromagnetic waves* with wavelengths in the range of about 1 pm to 1 fm, having shorter wavelengths than *X-rays* in the *electromagnetic spectrum.*

■ Gamma rays are produced by the de-excitation of a nucleus and frequently accompany the emission of *alpha radiation* or *beta radiation* from a nucleus. Gamma ray *photons* travel at the speed of light and have no charge or rest mass. Hence they cause comparatively little ionisation in matter and are highly penetrating. Several centimetres of lead or metres of concrete are required to absorb gamma rays. Gamma radiation may be detected using photographic films, *Geiger–Müller tubes* or *scintillation counters.* High-energy gamma ray photons are very penetrating and when absorbed in living tissue, cause a health hazard. Cells may be damaged, resulting in tumours, or they may be killed.

■ *e.g.* The fact that gamma radiation is highly penetrating gives rise to its use for the detection of irregularities in metals, pipes, etc. Medical uses include diagnosis in deep-body structures and radiotherapy.

■ *TIP* Gamma rays and X-rays are distinguishable only from their origins: gamma rays are produced as a result of nuclear de-excitation; X-rays are associated with the de-excitation of inner electrons or the rapid acceleration of charged particles.

gas: one of the four states of matter.

■ The molecules of a substance in the gaseous state have negligible forces between them. Consequently, a gas has no fixed shape or volume since it will always fully occupy the vessel into which it is placed. The molecules of a gas are in

g

random motion and collide with each other and the walls of the vessel. It is these collisions with walls of the vessel that give rise to the pressure of the gas. There is little to distinguish a gas from a vapour. It is frequently said that a vapour may be condensed by merely increasing the pressure. A gas must be cooled before pressure is applied in order to liquefy it. In general, the density of a gas is about one thousand times less than that of a *liquid* or a *solid*. This suggests that the mean separation of molecules in a gas is about ten times greater than that in a liquid or a solid. (See also *condensation; ideal gas; Brownian motion*.)

gas constant, molar: see *molar gas constant*.

γ-decay: see *gamma decay*.

Geiger–Müller tube: equipment used for the detection of ionising radiation.

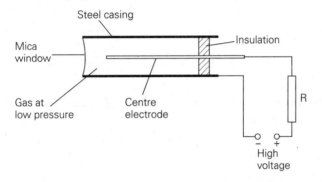

■ An electrode set along the axis of the tube is maintained at a high potential with respect to the outer metal casing. When ionising radiation enters the tube, the low-pressure gas in the tube undergoes *ionisation*. These ions are accelerated towards the centre electrode and the casing, depending on the sign of their charge. The ions collide with gas atoms, causing further ionisation. Consequently, a pulse of current is produced and a voltage pulse is detected across the resistor R. These pulses can be amplified and counted.

■ *TIP* The Geiger–Müller tube is the means by which the radiation is detected. A separate counter is required to count the voltage pulses. Strictly speaking, the whole apparatus should be referred to as a 'Geiger–Müller tube and counter'. However, it is frequently called a 'Geiger counter'.

giga-: prefix used with a unit to denote the multiple of $\times 10^9$; its symbol is G.

■ e.g. 1 gigawatt = 1×10^9 W = 1 GW. Gigawatts are frequently used to measure the output power of electrical generating stations.

GM tube: see *Geiger–Müller tube*.

γ-radiation: see *gamma radiation*.

gradient of a graph: the slope of a graph at a particular point.

■ Gradient m is given by

$$m = \frac{\text{change in } y\text{-value}}{\text{change in } x\text{-value}} = \frac{\Delta y}{\Delta x}$$

For a straight-line graph, the gradient can be determined by drawing a right-angled triangle with the line as the hypotenuse. The lengths of the other two sides are measured. If the graph line is a curve, then a tangent to the curve must be drawn at the point in question. The triangle for the calculation of the gradient is then drawn on this tangent.

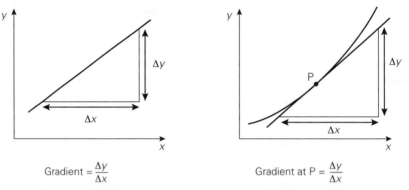

$$\text{Gradient} = \frac{\Delta y}{\Delta x} \qquad\qquad \text{Gradient at P} = \frac{\Delta y}{\Delta x}$$

■ *e.g.* Speed can be calculated from the gradient of a distance–time graph; acceleration from a velocity–time graph.

■ *TIP* In order to have sufficient reliability when calculating the gradient, the triangle drawn should have a hypotenuse of length at least half the length of the graph line.

grating element: the separation of corresponding points on two adjacent slits of a *diffraction grating.*

■ For a grating having N lines per unit length, the grating element d is given by
$$d = 1/N$$

■ *TIP* If the number of lines is given as N per metre, then $1/N = d$ has the unit metre.

gravitation: the attraction between any two masses within the universe.

■ The nature of the forces between masses is summarised in *Newton's law of gravitation.*

gravitational constant: see *universal constant of gravitation.*

gravitational field: a region of space where a mass experiences a force. The direction of the field is the direction of the force on the mass.

■ The magnitude of the gravitational force depends on the size of the mass. It does not depend on whether the object is moving or stationary or whether it is charged. Since gravitation is a mutual force between any two masses, there is a gravitational field surrounding every mass.

■ *e.g.* Effects of a gravitational field include *weight* and the *acceleration of free fall.*

gravitational field lines: lines representing the direction of a force on a point mass in a *gravitational field.*

■ Field lines never touch or cross. Diverging lines represent a field decreasing in strength and, conversely, converging lines represent a field increasing in strength. The gravitational field represented in the diagram is of particular importance. For a spherical uniform mass, the field lines appear to converge on the centre of the sphere. Thus, for any point outside the sphere, the sphere behaves as if all its mass were concentrated at its centre. This approximation is frequently used for astronomical bodies (sun, Earth, moon).

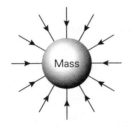

Gravitational field due to a spherical mass

■ *TIP* The point-mass approximation holds only for regions outside the sphere.

gravitational field strength: the force per unit mass acting on a small mass placed at a point in the gravitational field; it is usually given the symbol g.

■ Gravitational field strength may be defined by the word equation

$$\text{gravitational field strength } g = \frac{\text{gravitational force } F}{\text{mass } m}$$

The SI unit for gravitational field strength is newton per kilogram (N kg^{-1}). Gravitational field strength is a *vector* quantity. Since gravitational forces are always attractive, the direction of a gravitational field is always associated with attraction. According to *Newton's second law*

force = mass × acceleration

so the *acceleration of free fall* is numerically equal to the gravitational field strength.

■ *TIP* Some examination questions ask for differences between the various types of *force-field*. Remember that gravitational field strength is always associated with an attractive force only (compare with electrostatics, where the forces may be attractive or repulsive).

gravitational potential: the gravitational potential at a point is the work done per unit mass in bringing a point mass from infinity to that point.

■ Gravitational potential is a *scalar quantity* and its SI unit is joule per kilogram (J kg^{-1}). The gravitational potential at infinity is defined as being zero. Therefore, since gravitational forces are always attractive, work is done by the point mass as it moves from infinity and so all potentials are negative. The gravitational potential ϕ at a distance r from a point mass M is given by

$\phi = -GM/r$

where G is the *universal constant of gravitation*. Note that, if the potential at a point is ϕ, then the work done W in moving a mass m from infinity to that point is

$$W = \phi m$$

gravitational potential energy: the gravitational potential energy of a mass at a point is the work done on the mass in moving it from infinity to that point.

■ If the *gravitational potential* at a point is ϕ, then the gravitational potential energy of a mass m at that point is given by

$$\text{gravitational potential energy} = -\phi m$$

Gravitational potential energy is measured in joule (J) in the SI system. Its value is negative because, by convention, the zero of gravitational potential energy is taken to be zero at infinity. Since all gravitational forces are attractive, work is done by the mass as it moves from infinity and thus the work done on the mass is negative. Near to the Earth's surface, of most interest are changes in gravitational potential energy when a mass is raised or lowered vertically. For a mass m moved through a vertical distance Δh, the change in gravitational potential energy ΔE_p is given by

$$\Delta E_p = mg\Delta h$$

where g is the *acceleration of free fall*, assumed constant over the distance Δh.

■ *TIP* Although the zero of gravitational potential energy is taken as being at infinity, for convenience we often choose an alternative zero. For example, when raising a crate of mass 12 kg from floor level on to a shelf at a height of 1.7 m, we might say that the potential energy of the crate is $(12 \times 9.8 \times 1.7) = 200$ J. That is, we have assumed a zero of potential energy at floor level, rather than talking about the change in gravitational potential energy.

γ-ray: see *gamma radiation*.

ground state: when the energy of an extra-nuclear *electron* within an atom is at its minimum, the electron is said to be in its ground state.

hadron: a particle composed of either two or of three *quarks*.

■ *Baryons* (*protons* and *neutrons*) are composed of three quarks, whereas *mesons* contain two quarks. Hadrons are not regarded as fundamental particles in themselves because they are made up of quarks.

half-life: the half-life of a radioactive nuclide is the time taken for half the nuclei in a sample of the nuclide to decay; it is given the symbol $t_{\frac{1}{2}}$ and its SI unit is the second (s).

■ Note that half-life may be defined as the time for the activity of a sample of the nuclide to be halved. The nature of the decay curve is exponential.

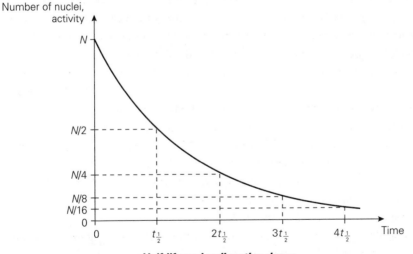

Half-life and radioactive decay

Half-life $t_{\frac{1}{2}}$ is related to the *radioactive decay constant* λ by the expression

$$\lambda\, t_{\frac{1}{2}} = \ln 2 = 0.693$$

(See also *randomness*; *spontaneity*.)

■ *TIP* When defining half-life, make sure you stress that it is the number of nuclei (or the activity) of the particular nuclide. Remember that, when the nuclei decay, the daughter products may also be radioactive. The half-life of some nuclides is very long. Consequently, half-life can be expressed in years.

half-wave rectification: see *rectification*.

Hall effect: when a magnetic field acts at right angles to a slice of a current-carrying material, a potential difference (Hall voltage, V_H) is created at right-angles to both the current and the magnetic field.

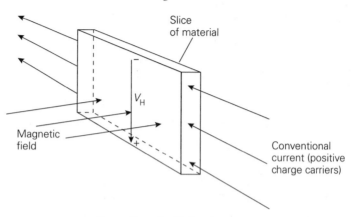

Formation of a Hall voltage

■ Since the *charge carriers* in the slice of material are moving at right angles to a magnetic field, there is a force acting on them, the direction being given by *Fleming's left-hand rule*. This force creates a greater concentration of charged particles along one edge of the slice and hence a difference in potential across the slice — the Hall voltage V_H. The magnitude of the Hall voltage is determined by the concentration of charge carriers, the current and the magnetic flux density. If all other factors are kept constant, the magnitude of the Hall voltage may be used as a means of measuring magnetic flux density.

Hall probe: an instrument used to measure magnetic flux density.

■ The instrument is based on the principle of the *Hall effect*. The probe, containing a thin slice of a *semiconductor* material, is placed in the magnetic field and rotated to give a maximum meter reading. The meter reading is calibrated directly to read flux density normal to the probe.

heat capacity: see *thermal capacity*.

heat engine: a machine which receives thermal energy at a high temperature, converts as much of it as possible into useful work and passes the remainder to cooler surroundings.

■ The theoretical *efficiency* of such an engine depends on the temperatures at which it operates. If thermal energy Q_H is received at thermodynamic temperature T_H and an amount Q_L is removed at thermodynamic temperature T_L, the useful work done is $(Q_H - Q_L)$ and the efficiency is given by

$$\text{efficiency} = (Q_H - Q_L)/Q_H = (T_H - T_L)/T_H$$

Note that the actual efficiency will be less than the theoretical efficiency. The efficiency can never be 100% because T_L can never be $0\,\text{K}$.

heating: a transfer of energy to an object resulting in an increase in the random kinetic or potential energies of the atoms or molecules of the object.

■ The increase is observed as either a rise in temperature or an increase in the internal energy of the object.

■ *e.g.* Heating (thermal energy supplied) is one factor in the *first law of thermodynamics*.

■ *TIP* Heating is a process. It is appropriate at AS/A-level to think of thermal energy being transferred when an object is being heated.

heat pump: a machine to pump thermal energy from a lower temperature to a higher temperature.

■ *e.g.* A refrigerator uses a heat pump to remove thermal energy from the ice compartment and supply it to the outside air, which is at a higher temperature.

■ *TIP* Work must be done to move thermal energy from a lower to a higher temperature.

heavy damping: see *damping, degrees of.*

helical spring: a spring formed by winding a wire round a cylinder.

■ The usefulness of a helical spring is that, so long as the elastic limit is not exceeded, *Hooke's law* is obeyed and force F is proportional to extension x, i.e.

$$F = kx$$

where k is the *spring constant*.

■ *e.g.* A mass–spring system for the measurement of the acceleration of free fall; the newton-meter.

■ *TIP* There are other types of spring in common use in laboratories such as a *spiral spring*, found in moving-coil meters. However, where the type of spring is not specified, reference is usually being made to a helical spring.

hertz, Hz: the SI unit of frequency:

1 hertz = 1 oscillation per second.

■ *TIP* Remember that the hertz is associated with oscillations. Do not confuse hertz with *becquerel*, the unit of activity. The becquerel is associated with counts per unit time, not oscillations.

homogeneity: when applied to equations, homogeneity means that each term in the equation must correspond to the same physical quantity.

■ In the equation

$$s = ut + \tfrac{1}{2}at^2$$

we know that the terms are s, ut and $\frac{1}{2}at^2$. Each of the terms must be the same physical quantity. In this case, s is distance travelled and so ut and $\frac{1}{2}at^2$ must also each represent distance.

Hooke's law: *stress* is proportional to *strain*, provided the *elastic limit* has not been exceeded.

■ For a sample of material that does not change significantly in cross-sectional area, Hooke's law is simplified to become 'force is proportional to extension, provided that the elastic limit has not been exceeded'. Hooke's law is frequently applied to the extension of springs under load. (See also *spring constant; Young modulus.*)

Hubble constant: see *Hubble's law.*

Hubble's law: the speed of recession of a galaxy is proportional to its distance from Earth.

■ For a galaxy at distance d from Earth and receding at speed v,

$$v = H_0 d$$

where H_0 is the Hubble constant. Since it is difficult to measure astronomical distances with precision, there is doubt about the precise value of H_0. It is generally accepted to be about $75 \text{ km s}^{-1} \text{ Mpc}^{-1}$. This means that, for each million parsecs to a galaxy, the galaxy's speed away from Earth increases by 75 km s^{-1}.

■ **e.g.** Hubble's law may be used to estimate the age of the *universe*.

hysteresis: a term applied to a material under stress. Hysteresis means that when the material is stressed elastically, the stress–strain curve does not have the same shape as when the stress is removed.

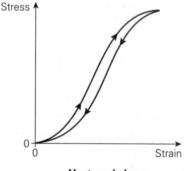

Hysteresis loop

■ The area enclosed within the loop (the hysteresis loop) is a measure of the energy expended during one complete cycle of the application and removal of the stress.

■ **TIP** Hysteresis is a phenomenon observed in magnetism. If a magnetic material is magnetised and then demagnetised, energy is expended.

ice point: the temperature of a mixture of pure water and melting ice in thermal equilibrium at *standard atmospheric pressure*.

■ By definition, this temperature is zero degrees Centigrade (0°C). It is 273.15 K.

ideal gas: a gas that obeys the gas laws (*Boyle's law, Charles's law* and the *pressure law*) or the *ideal gas law* at all values of volume, pressure and temperature.

■ Such a gas does not exist, since all gases deviate from the gas laws to a greater or lesser extent. However, for a gas at relatively low pressure and at a temperature well in excess of its boiling point, the gas does approximate to the ideal. For example, oxygen and nitrogen at room temperature and a few atmospheres pressure do approximate quite well. Remember that the early experiments were conducted with air! (See also *kinetic theory of gases*.)

ideal gas equation: see *ideal gas law*.

ideal gas law (also called 'ideal gas equation'): an equation relating the pressure, volume and temperature of an *ideal gas*.

■ For n mol of an ideal gas having a volume V at pressure p and thermodynamic temperature T

$$pV = nRT$$

where R is a constant known as the *molar gas constant* ($R = 8.31 \, \text{J K}^{-1} \text{mol}^{-1}$). The law applies to any mass, measured in moles, of an ideal gas. If the pressure p_1, volume V_1 and thermodynamic temperature T_1 of a fixed mass of gas are changed to pressure p_2, volume V_2 and thermodynamic temperature T_2, then the equation may be written in the form

$$p_1 V_1 / T_1 = p_2 V_2 / T_2$$

This form of the equation is very useful where changes are being made to a fixed mass of gas.

■ *TIP* If you are asked about the ideal gas law, then your answer should be based on the equation $pV = nRT$.

image in a plane mirror: an image that may be traced using the laws of *reflection of light*.

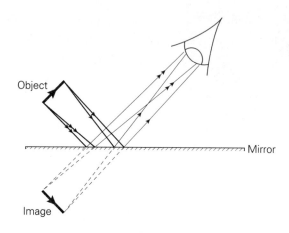

- a *virtual image*
- laterally inverted (left to right)
- erect
- the same size as the object
- the same distance from the mirror as the object
- directly behind the object; that is, the line joining object to image is at right angles to the mirror

■ *e.g.* Avoidance of *parallax error* when reading a scale.

■ *TIP* Remember that the image is laterally inverted. Do not be tempted to say 'inverted', because that would also mean 'upside-down'.

impulse: the product of a force F acting on an object and the time Δt for which the force acts:

$$\text{impulse} = F\Delta t$$

■ *Newton's second law of motion* relates force to rate of change of momentum $\Delta p/\Delta t$, that is

$$F = \Delta p/\Delta t$$

Thus

$$\text{impulse} = F\Delta t = \Delta p$$

The impulse acting on an object that is free to move is equal to its change in momentum. Impulse has the same unit as momentum; in the SI system, the unit may be quoted as kilogram metre per second (kg m s^{-1}) or newton second (N s).

■ *TIP* In everyday language, an impulse implies that the effect takes place in a short period of time. In physics, the time Δt may be short (as in a collision) or long (as in the firing of a rocket engine).

indicator diagram: a graph showing the variation of pressure with volume for a system.

One such diagram for air in a cylinder is shown below. During the change AB, the air is compressed, work being done on the air. It is then heated at constant volume during BC. The air then expands (CD), doing external work before it is cooled during DA to return it to its starting point. The air has passed through a complete cycle. The useful work done by the air is represented by the area ABCD.

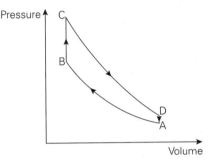

induced emf: an *electromotive force* (emf) generated in a conductor whenever the conductor cuts magnetic field lines or a magnetic field changes around the conductor, i.e. there is a change in *magnetic flux linkage* (see also *electromagnetic induction*; *Faraday's laws of electromagnetic induction*).

inelastic collision: a collision in which kinetic energy is not conserved.

Some of the initial kinetic energy of the colliding objects is converted into some other form (e.g. thermal energy). As in any collision, linear momentum and total energy are always conserved.

infrared radiation (IR): *electromagnetic waves* with wavelengths in the range of about 1 mm to 700 nm, lying between *microwaves* and visible *light* in the *electromagnetic spectrum*.

Infrared radiation is emitted by all bodies above 0 K. The spectrum of the radiation and its intensity is dependent on the nature and temperature of the surface of the body. Consequently, infrared radiation is used for the detection of hot bodies and for surveying the Earth from satellites. The radiation may be detected with photodiodes or by means of its heating effect.

insulator, electrical: a material that does not contain any free-moving charge carriers.

Electrical insulators do not conduct an electric current. However, their insulating properties may fail when a large *electric field* is applied. Electrons are then stripped off atoms and these then move, constituting a current.

intensity: the intensity of a wave is the wave energy incident per unit time per unit area normal to the wave.

In the SI system, intensity is measured in watts per metre squared (W m^{-2}). Intensity of a *sinusoidal* wave is proportional to the square of the *amplitude* of the wave. For monochromatic light, the intensity is proportional to the number of *photons* passing per unit time through unit area. If the frequency of the light increases, then, for constant intensity, the number of photons per unit time per unit area decreases.

■ *e.g.* Intensity is an important factor when considering the *photoelectric effect.*

intercept: the point at which the line of a graph cuts the y-axis for $x = 0$ (the y-intercept) or the point where the line of a graph cuts the x-axis for $y = 0$ (the x-intercept).

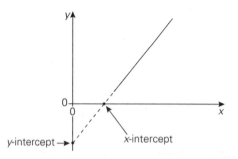

Intercepts on a graph

■ *TIP* In order to read off an intercept from a graph, the origin of the graph must be shown.

interference: an effect that occurs when two or more waves overlap to produce a new wave pattern, i.e. a change in *amplitude.*

■ Interference patterns provide evidence for the wave nature of electromagnetic waves.

■ *e.g. Destructive interference, constructive interference, two-source interference* (see also *coherence*).

■ *TIP* Interference is explained in terms of the *principle of superposition.* Interference is the result of superposition, provided that certain conditions are fulfilled.

internal energy: the sum of the random kinetic and potential energies of the individual molecules of an object.

■ An increase in internal energy results in either a rise in temperature or a change of state of the object. Increasing the kinetic energy of the molecules is accompanied by a rise in temperature. Changing state (melting, boiling, freezing, etc.) involves changes in bond energy between molecules and hence changes in potential energy. An ideal gas has no intermolecular forces and therefore its internal energy consists of only kinetic energy. Generally, changes in internal energy are more important than the total internal energy of the object. Internal energy may be changed by either heating the object or doing work. (See also *thermal capacity.*)

TIP The definition makes reference to 'random' kinetic and potential energies; the kinetic energy of an object as it is falling towards Earth is not random and so is not internal energy.

internal resistance: the resistance to movement of charge (current) within an electrical power source.

The effect of internal resistance is to reduce the potential difference between the terminals of the supply (the terminal potential difference) when the supply is delivering a current.

For a supply of *electromotive force* (emf) E and terminal potential difference V, the potential difference across the internal resistance V_r is given by

$$V_r = E - V$$

The potential difference V_r is sometimes referred to as *lost volts* and if the supply is delivering current I, then, by Ohm's law

$$\text{lost volts } V_r = Ir$$

where r is the internal resistance of the supply. Internal resistance is responsible for energy losses within the supply itself. In dry batteries, internal resistance increases as the battery 'runs down'.

TIP Any supply delivers maximum power to the external circuit when the external resistance of the circuit is equal to the internal resistance of the supply.

ionisation: the process whereby neutral atoms lose electrons to become charged particles or ions.

Ionisation may come about as a result of heating, application of large electric fields or bombarding with high-energy particles. When an electron is removed from a neutral atom, the electron is said to be a negative ion and the remainder of the atom is a positive ion.

e.g. Ionisation associated with *alpha particles, beta particles* and *gamma radiation,* and their detection using a *Geiger–Müller tube.*

IR: see *infrared radiation.*

isothermal change: a change in the pressure and volume of a system such that thermal energy is allowed to enter or leave the system in order to maintain constant temperature.

In practice, such a change takes place when the change is made slowly and the containing vessel has thin conducting walls. (See also *Boyle's law.*)

isotopes: two or more forms of the same element, having the same number of *protons* but different numbers of *neutrons* in their nuclei.

Isotopes of an element have the same *proton number* but different *nucleon numbers*. Different isotopes may be identified by giving the name of the element and its nucleon number.

e.g. Neon-20 and neon-22 are two isotopes of neon.

I/V characteristics: see *current–voltage characteristics.*

JET nuclear fusion project: JET (Joint European Torus) is Europe's attempt to control the *nuclear fusion* reaction of isotopes of hydrogen in order to maintain a continuous reaction.

■ The torus was built at Culham in Oxfordshire, UK. In 1992, JET generated more energy than was supplied for a very short period of time, but there is still much research to be done before the method will be efficient enough to generate electricity. The main problem is the containment of the *plasma*.

joule, J: the SI unit of energy or work done.

■ One joule of work is done when a force of one newton moves its point of application by one metre in the direction of the force. The joule may be expressed as the newton metre (Nm). Its base units are $\text{kg}\,\text{m}^2\,\text{s}^{-2}$.

■ *TIP* When defining the joule, make sure that you mention the direction of movement of the force.

kelvin, K: the SI unit of temperature difference.

■ It is defined as the fraction 1/273.16 of the difference in temperature between the *absolute zero* and the *triple point* of water.

Kelvin scale of temperature: see *thermodynamic scale of temperature*.

kilo-: prefix used with a unit to denote the multiple of $\times 10^3$. Its symbol is k.

■ *e.g.* Electric power is often measured in kilowatts. 1 kilowatt = 1×10^3 W = 1 kW.

kilowatt-hour, kW h: a unit of energy.

■ It is not an SI unit but is widely used as a practical unit (e.g. in the home, where electrical energy suppliers refer to the kilowatt-hour as the 'Unit'). One kilowatt-hour is the work done when an appliance transfers work at a rate of 1000 W (1000 J s^{-1}) for a time of 1 hour.

$$1\,\text{kW h} = 1\,\text{kW} \times 1\,\text{h}$$
$$= 1000\,\text{W} \times (60 \times 60)\,\text{s}$$
$$= 3.6 \times 10^6\,\text{J}$$
$$= 3.6\,\text{MJ}$$

kinetic energy: the energy of a mass due to its motion.

■ The kinetic energy E_k of a body of mass m moving at speed v is given by
$$E_k = \tfrac{1}{2}mv^2$$
Kinetic energy is a *scalar quantity* and, in the *SI system*, is measured in joule (J).

■ *e.g.* The energy of the molecules of an *ideal gas* is wholly kinetic.

■ *TIP* Kinetic energy is proportional to (speed)^2. A doubling of speed means four times the kinetic energy. Similarly, increasing speed from 10 m s^{-1} to 20 m s^{-1} requires only one-fifth the energy required to increase speed from 70 m s^{-1} to 80 m s^{-1}.

kinetic theory of gases: a model of gases used to explain why they obey the gas laws.

■ Assumptions, or postulates, are made about the nature of gas molecules and then *Newton's laws of motion* are applied in order to predict their behaviour. The assumptions (postulates) of the kinetic theory of gases are:

● all gases consist of a very large number of atoms or molecules

- the atoms or molecules behave as if they are hard, perfectly elastic, identical spheres
- there are no forces of attraction or repulsion between atoms or molecules unless they are in collision with each other or with the walls of the containing vessel
- the motion of the atoms or molecules is totally random
- the total volume of the atoms or molecules is negligible compared with the volume of the containing vessel
- the time of collisions is negligible compared with the time between collisions

For an ideal gas containing n molecules per unit volume, each of mass m and having a *mean square speed* $<c^2>$, it can be shown that the pressure p of the gas is given by

$$p = \tfrac{1}{3}nm <c^2>$$

Since the density ρ of the gas will be given by $\rho = nm$, then

$$p = \tfrac{1}{3}\rho <c^2>$$

If the equation $p = \tfrac{1}{3}nm <c^2>$ is combined with the *ideal gas equation*, then it can be shown that

$$\tfrac{1}{2}m <c^2> = \tfrac{3}{2}kT$$

where k is a constant and T is the thermodynamic temperature. The constant k is known as the *Boltzmann constant* and is equal to $1.38 \times 10^{-23}\,\mathrm{J\,K^{-1}}$. The equation is important in that it links the mean kinetic energy $\tfrac{1}{2}m<c^2>$ of a molecule to the temperature of the gas.

■ *TIP* If you are asked to give the assumptions, make sure you state that it is the total volume (not the volume of a single molecule) that is negligible compared with the volume of the containing vessel. In some books you will find that 'kinetic energy is proportional to the thermodynamic temperature' is given as an assumption. This is not so. This relationship is based on the other assumptions and the ideal gas equation.

Kirchhoff's first law: the sum of the currents entering any junction in an electric circuit is equal to the sum of the currents leaving that junction.

■ For the junction shown in the diagram

$$I_1 + I_2 = I_3 + I_4$$

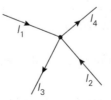

Kirchhoff's first law is a consequence of the law of conservation of charge. Since electric current is rate of flow of charge then, for charge to be conserved, rate of flow must also be conserved.

Kirchhoff's second law: in any closed loop in an electric circuit, the algebraic sum of the *electromotive forces* in the loop is equal to the algebraic sum of the *potential differences* in that loop.

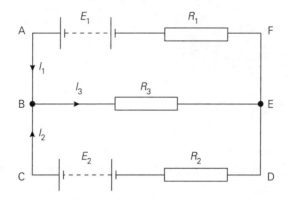

In the diagram, for the loop ABEFA

$$E_1 = I_3R_3 + I_1R_1$$

and for the loop ACDFA

$$E_1 - E_2 = -I_2R_2 + I_1R_1$$

Kirchhoff's second law is a consequence of the law of *conservation of energy*. An emf represents energy per unit charge converted (transferred) into electrical energy from some other form, whereas a potential difference represents energy converted (transferred) from electrical to some other form. Clearly, energy input to the circuit must equal energy output from the circuit.

laminar flow: see *streamline flow*.

laser: a source of monochromatic radiation in the visible, *infrared* or *ultraviolet* regions of the *electromagnetic spectrum*.

■ The letters ***laser*** stand for **l**ight **a**mplification by the **s**timulated **e**mission of **r**adiation. Laser light is coherent and is emitted in a parallel beam (see *coherence*). The beam may be of relatively high intensity and if viewed directly, may well cause damage to the retina of the eye, even blindness.

latent heat of fusion: see *specific latent heat*.

latent heat of vaporisation: see *specific latent heat*.

ldr: see *light-dependent resistor*.

led: see *light-emitting diode*.

length: a *base quantity* in the *SI system*; its unit is the metre (m).

■ One metre is the distance travelled by light in a vacuum in a time of 1/299 792 458 second.

lens formula: a relationship between the object distance u, the image distance v and the *focal length f* of a lens.

$$1/u + 1/v = 1/f$$

To allow the formula to be used in all situations, a sign convention is employed:
- real objects and real images have positive values for u and v, respectively
- virtual objects and virtual images have negative values for u and v, respectively
- converging lenses have a positive value for f
- diverging lenses have a negative value for f

Lenz's law: see *electromagnetic induction, laws of*.

lepton: a group of fundamental particles including the *electron*.

■ These light particles are associated with the *weak nuclear force*.

light: more correctly referred to as visible light. Light consists of *transverse waves* in the visible spectrum, which is one small part of the *electromagnetic spectrum*.

■ The eye is sensitive to electromagnetic waves in this part of the spectrum, interpreting change in wavelength (or frequency) as a change in colour. The range of wavelengths detected by the eye varies with individuals but is generally accepted as 700 nm for red light (frequency 4.3×10^{14} Hz) to 400 nm for violet light (frequency 7.5×10^{14} Hz).

light damping: see *damping, degrees of.*

light-dependent resistor (ldr): a resistor whose *resistance* decreases as the *intensity* of light falling on it increases.

▓ The change in resistance with light intensity is non-linear and typically

resistance in moonlight ≈ 2 MΩ

resistance in bright sunlight $\approx 200 \, \Omega$

▓ *e.g.* Light-dependent resistors are used in *potential divider* circuits for the monitoring of light intensity.

light-emitting diode (led): a *diode* that emits light when it is forward biased, i.e. conducting a current.

▓ The diode does not emit light when it is not conducting. Generally, a potential difference of about 2 V must be applied to the diode before it conducts and emits light. The light emitted by a particular diode is of one colour. Light-emitting diodes use relatively little power and, being solid, are robust. They are frequently used as warning lights on instrument panels.

light-year, ly: a non-SI unit of distance used in astronomy, which is equal to the distance that light will travel in a vacuum in one year.

▓ Since light travels at a speed of 3.00×10^{8} m s^{-1} in a vacuum and there are 3.15×10^{7} s in one year, 1 light-year is equal to 9.45×10^{15} m. Other units of distance used in astrophysics are the *parsec* and the *astronomical unit.*

▓ *TIP* The light-year is a unit of distance, not time.

limit of proportionality: when the stress applied to a sample of material is plotted against strain, limit of proportionality is the point on the graph at which the line is no longer straight (see also *Hooke's law; elastic limit*).

line spectrum: see *emission spectrum; absorption spectrum.*

liquid: one of the four states of matter.

▓ A liquid is characterised by the fact that it has a fixed volume but no fixed shape. There are forces of attraction between the molecules (hence the fixed volume) but the rigid forces seen in a *solid* no longer exist, so the molecules can move throughout the body of the liquid. A liquid and a solid have approximately the same density, suggesting that the separation of molecules is about the same in both. The separation of molecules is about one-tenth of that in a *gas.*

liquid-in-glass thermometer: a general-purpose direct-reading thermometer.

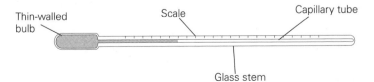

Thin-walled bulb   Scale   Capillary tube

Glass stem

■ The temperature range of the thermometer depends on the liquid used. Mercury-in-glass thermometers can be used from about −20°C to about +350°C. If the liquid is ethanol, the range is about −100°C to +50°C. The sensitivity, i.e. the distance between scale markings on the stem of the thermometer, depends on the volume of the bulb and the bore of the stem. Its thermal capacity and response time are relatively large and therefore it cannot be used for measuring rapidly changing temperatures or the temperature of a small object. Other types of thermometer include the *thermistor thermometer* and the *thermocouple thermometer*.

longitudinal wave: a wave in which the displacements of the particles in the wave are along the direction of transfer of energy of the wave.

Direction of
displacement

Direction of
energy transfer

Direction of displacement in a longitudinal wave

■ The oscillations of the particles in the wave give rise to regions where the particles are closer together than normal. These regions are known as *compressions*, since the pressure is above normal. Conversely, regions where the particles are more widely spaced are also created. These regions are known as *rarefactions*, since the pressure is below normal.

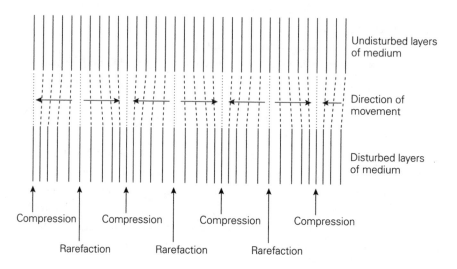

Compressions and rarefactions in a longitudinal wave

■ *e.g.* Sound waves.

■ *TIP* When stating what is meant by a longitudinal wave, be very careful to specify 'direction of transfer of energy of the wave', not merely 'direction of the wave'.

lost volts: the difference between the electromotive force (emf) of an electrical supply and its terminal potential difference.

lost volts = emf − terminal potential difference

■ Lost volts arise because the supply has to provide a potential difference in order to drive current through the supply itself. The lost volts constitute the potential difference across the *internal resistance* of the supply.

machine: a device that either transforms energy into a more useful form or changes the magnitude of a force (see also *efficiency; conservation of energy*).

■ *e.g.* The engine of a car may be thought of as being a machine in that it converts chemical energy into kinetic energy of the moving vehicle. Nutcrackers apply large forces to a nut when smaller forces are applied at the ends of the handles.

■ *TIP* It must be remembered that it is not possible to obtain 'something for nothing'. More energy has to be put into the machine than is obtained as useful output work.

magnetic field: a region of space where a magnetic pole, a current-carrying conductor or a moving charged particle will experience a force.

■ Magnetic fields are produced by magnets or by current-carrying conductors. A magnetic field is represented by a series of lines, each having a direction. Each line gives the direction in which a 'free' north pole would move in the magnetic field. Magnetic field lines can never touch or cross. The closeness of the lines indicates the strength of the field.

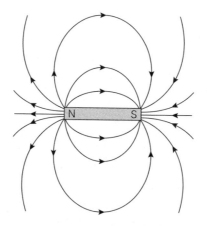

Magnetic field due to a bar magnet

■ *e.g.* *Fleming's left-hand rule* and the *motor effect* are used in order to distinguish a magnetic field from an *electric field*.

■ *TIP* A magnetic field may be distinguished from an electric field in that a charged particle experiences a force in a magnetic field only when it is moving. In an electric field, the same force acts on the charged particle whether it is stationary or moving. Do not forget that the field lines have direction.

magnetic field due to a coil or solenoid: see *magnetic flux density due to a coil*.

magnetic field due to a current-carrying conductor: see *magnetic flux density due to a long straight wire*.

magnetic field strength: see *magnetic flux density*.

magnetic flux: the product of the *magnetic flux density* and the area normal to the field through which the field is passing.

■ For a magnetic flux density B at an angle θ to an area A, the magnetic flux ϕ is given by the equation

$\phi = BA \sin\theta$

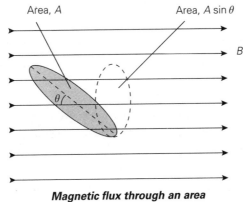

Magnetic flux through an area

The SI unit of magnetic flux is the weber (Wb) which is tesla metre squared (1 Wb = 1 T m^2). If magnetic flux density is modelled as the number of lines of magnetic force per unit area, then magnetic flux is the total number of lines passing through an area. Magnetic flux is a concept vital for the understanding of electromagnetic induction.

magnetic flux density (also called 'magnetic field strength'): a measure of the magnitude (strength) of a magnetic field.

■ Lines of magnetic force (flux lines) are used to represent a magnetic field, and the closer together the lines, the stronger the field. Magnetic flux density can be thought of as the number of lines of magnetic force passing normally through unit area. In the SI system, magnetic flux density is defined by reference to the *motor effect*. The unit of magnetic flux density is the *tesla* (T) or weber per metre squared (Wb m^{-2}). (See also *magnetic flux; magnetic flux linkage; electromagnetic induction*.)

magnetic flux density due to a coil: the strength of a magnetic field caused by a current-carrying coil; the usual coils that are studied are the flat coil and the solenoid.

■ The flux density B at the centre of a flat coil of radius r having N turns is given by

$$B = \mu_0 NI/2r$$

where μ_0 is the *permeability of free space*. The flux density B along the axis of a long solenoid having n turns per unit length is given by

$$B = \mu_0 nI$$

In each case, the flux density is calculated on the axis of the coil, at its centre. The formulae assume that the coils are in a vacuum, though, in practice, the formulae also apply to coils in air.

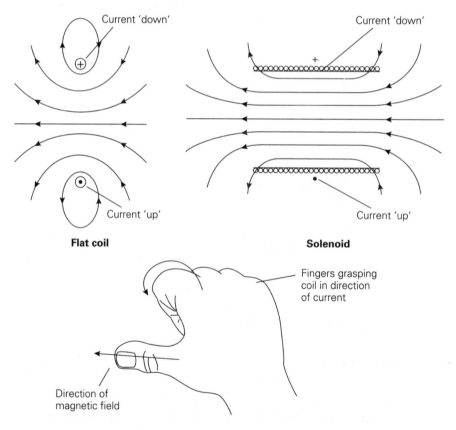

Magnetic field due to a flat coil and a solenoid

The direction of the magnetic field is found using the right-hand grip rule: if you imagine grasping the coil in your right hand, with your fingers pointing in the direction of the current, then your thumb gives the direction of the magnetic field.

TIP When drawing a diagram of these magnetic fields, start by drawing a field line along the axis of the coil.

magnetic flux density due to a long straight wire: in a vacuum at a distance r from a wire carrying current I, magnetic flux density B is given by

$B = \mu_0 I / 2\pi r$

where μ_0 is the *permeability of free space*.

For a wire in air, the formula is correct to four significant figures. The direction of the magnetic field is given by Maxwell's corkscrew rule: if you imagine screwing a right-handed corkscrew in the direction of the current, the direction of motion of your thumb gives the direction of the magnetic field.

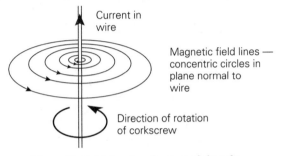

Magnetic field due to a long straight wire

TIP When drawing a diagram to represent the magnetic field, do not forget that the field lines are concentric circles, with increasing separation as distance from the wire increases — use a pair of compasses!

magnetic flux density due to a solenoid: see *magnetic flux density due to a coil.*

magnetic flux linkage (also called 'flux linkage')**:** the product, in a coil, of the magnetic flux passing through the coil and the number of turns on the coil.

Using the model of magnetic flux density as the number of lines of magnetic force per unit area, the magnetic flux ϕ is the total number of lines passing through, or linking, each turn of the coil. If this flux links N turns (the number of turns on the coil), then the magnetic flux linkage is $N\phi$. The unit of magnetic flux linkage is the weber (Wb), although to distinguish it from magnetic flux, it is frequently referred to as 'weber-turns'. Magnetic flux linkage is an important concept in the understanding of electromagnetic induction. (See also *Faraday's law of electromagnetic induction; Lenz's law.*)

magnets, law of: a simple law to determine whether magnetic poles attract or repel, namely:

- like poles repel
- unlike poles attract

magnification, linear: linear magnification produced by a lens where

$$\text{magnification } m = \frac{\text{length of image}}{\text{length of object}}$$

■ For an object, distance u from a lens with image distance v, the magnification m is given by

$$m = v/u$$

manometer: a device used to measure pressure difference.

■ It consists of a U-tube, partially filled with liquid of density ρ. One arm of the manometer is connected to the pressure supply and the other is left open to the atmosphere.

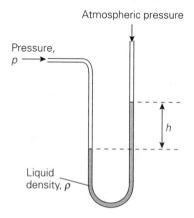

Using the formula for *pressure in a fluid*

pressure p = atmospheric pressure + $h\rho g$

where h is the difference in vertical height of the liquid levels and g is the acceleration of free fall. The pressure differences that can be measured are dependent on the length of each arm of the U-tube and the density of the liquid used.

mass: a base quantity in the SI system; its unit is the kilogram (kg).

■ It is a *scalar quantity* and is a measure of a body's resistance to change in velocity. Unless travelling at speeds close to the speed of light, mass is constant and does not depend on any gravitational field. The weight w of an object of mass m undergoing free fall with an acceleration g is given by

$$w = mg$$

■ *TIP* Do not confuse mass with *amount of substance*. The latter quantity is measured in *moles*.

mass defect: see *binding energy, nuclear; mass–energy equivalence*.

mass–energy equivalence: when an object acquires an amount of energy (for example, its kinetic energy increases), then its mass increases.

■ This is expressed in terms of the equation

$$\Delta E = c^2 \Delta m$$

where ΔE is the acquired energy, Δm is the increase in mass and c is the speed of light. (See also *mass defect; binding energy, nuclear*.)

■ *TIP* The word 'equivalence' is important. When the object slows down and loses kinetic energy, its mass decreases. The mass is not lost but it is dispersed as an equivalent amount of energy. Mass and energy are equivalent; there is no conversion from energy to mass or vice versa.

mass number: see *nucleon number.*

mass–spring system: a system consisting of a vertical helical spring, fixed at its upper end, from which is suspended a mass.

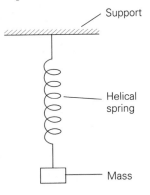

Support

Helical spring

Mass

■ For small vertical oscillations of the mass *m*, such that the amplitude of the oscillations is less than the static extension *e* of the spring, the period *T* of oscillation of the mass is given by

$$T = 2\pi\sqrt{(m/k)} = 2\pi\sqrt{(e/g)}$$

where *k* is the *spring constant* (elastic constant) of the spring and *g* is the *acceleration of free fall.*

■ *e.g.* The mass–spring system may be used to determine *k* dynamically rather than by the static extension of the spring. It may also be used to determine *g*.

■ *TIP* If you are asked to describe a method for the determination of *g* by free fall, do not describe a method involving a mass–spring system: a mass–spring system is not free fall.

material dispersion: the spreading out of a light pulse as it travels along an *optic fibre* owing to the light having different speeds in the fibre.

■ The *refractive index* of the material of the optic fibre depends on the wavelength of light. Since refractive index is determined by the speed of light in the material, then different wavelengths will have different speeds in the fibre. A short pulse of light entering a fibre will be spread out according to wavelength as it travels along the fibre. The problem of material dispersion can be overcome by using monochromatic light, as produced by a *laser.*

Maxwell's corkscrew rule: see *corkscrew rule, Maxwell's.*

mean kinetic energy: in an ideal gas the mean kinetic energy of a molecule is proportional to the thermodynamic temperature *T* and is given by the expression

$$\text{mean kinetic energy} = \tfrac{1}{2}m <c^2> = \tfrac{3}{2}kT$$

where *k* is the *Boltzmann constant.*

▨ Note that, at any particular temperature, molecules of different gases have the same mean kinetic energy if they can be treated as being ideal. Their mean square speeds $<c^2>$ would be different.

mean square speed: the mean, or average, value of the (molecular speed)^2; its symbol is $<c^2>$.

▨ If $c_1, c_2, c_3, c_4, c_5 \dots c_N$ are the speeds at any one time of N molecules of a gas, then the mean square speed is given by

$$<c^2> = (c_1{}^2 + c_2{}^2 + c_3{}^2 + c_4{}^2 + c_5{}^2 + \dots c_N{}^2)/N$$

Although mean square speed is defined above, it is never calculated using this equation. There are too many molecules! The value is, however, important in the development of the *kinetic theory of gases*.

▨ *e.g.* Mean square speed is important when considering *mean kinetic energy* of a gas molecule and *pressure of an ideal gas*.

▨ *TIP* Do not confuse mean square speed $<c^2>$ with the square of the mean speed $<c^2>$: they are not the same quantity.

mega-: prefix used with a unit to denote the multiple of $\times 10^6$; its symbol is M.

▨ *e.g.* 1 mega-electronvolt = 1×10^6 eV = 1 MeV. Mega-electronvolts may be used to measure nuclear binding energies.

melting (also called 'fusion'): the change in state of a substance from solid to liquid without any change in temperature.

▨ The melting process, or fusion, involves the absorption of thermal energy by the substance without any temperature rise — latent heat of fusion (see *specific latent heat*). This energy is needed to break some of the attractive bonds between atoms and molecules.

meson: a partical composed of two *quarks*.

▨ The *strong nuclear force* between nucleons is transmitted through the exchange of mesons. About 50 different types of meson have been discovered. Mesons together with *baryons* form the group of particles known as *hadrons*.

metre, m: the *base unit* of length in the *SI system*.

▨ The metre is defined as the distance travelled in a vacuum by light during a time interval of $1/299\ 792\ 458$ s, that is $1/c$, where c is the speed of light. Note that the speed of light in a vacuum cannot be measured. It is fixed by the definition of the metre.

▨ *TIP* Do not confuse the unit symbol m with the prefix m (milli-). The prefix does not have a space between it and the unit whereas the symbols for two units would have a space between them. For example, ms^{-1} would be 'per millisecond' whereas m s^{-1} is 'metres per second'.

micro-: prefix used with a unit to denote the sub-multiple of $\times 10^{-6}$; its symbol is μ.

▨ *e.g.* Capacitances are sometimes quoted in microfarads.

1 microfarad = 1×10^{-6} m = 1 μF

microwaves: *electromagnetic waves* with wavelengths in the range of about 10 cm to 1 mm, lying between *radio waves* and *infrared radiation* in the *electromagnetic spectrum*.

■ Microwaves may be focused and are used extensively for radar and for communication purposes, including satellite communication. Some microwaves are absorbed by water, where the wave energy is converted into thermal energy. Consequently, microwaves are hazardous to human health but are used in 'microwave ovens' for cooking.

milli-: prefix used with a unit to denote the sub-multiple of $\times 10^{-3}$; its symbol is m.

■ *e.g.* 1 millimetre = 1×10^{-3} m = 1 mm.

■ *TIP* Be careful not to leave a space between the prefix and the unit. The symbol m on its own represents metre. So, 2 ms means two milliseconds but 2 m s means two metre seconds.

Millikan's oil drop experiment: an experiment that enables the *elementary charge* to be determined.

■ Essentially, the apparatus consists of two horizontal metal plates between which there is a potential difference.

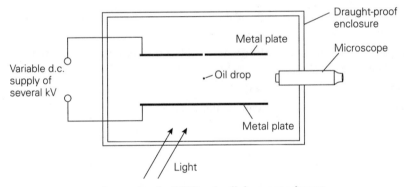

Apparatus for Millikan's oil drop experiment

Oil drops are introduced into the space between the plates through a hole in the top plate and then viewed using a microscope. The oil drops are charged by friction from an atomiser. First, the potential difference between the plates is adjusted until the drop is stationary. Under these circumstances

   apparent weight of drop = charge on drop $\times$ *electric field strength*

The drop is then allowed to fall freely under gravity and acquires a terminal speed due to viscous drag. The drag force is given by *Stokes' law*

   apparent weight of drop = viscous drag

Knowing the density of the oil and the viscosity of the air, the charge on the drop can be determined. Millikan measured the charges on many oil drops and found that the charge was always a multiple of 1.6×10^{-19} C. This value of charge was taken as the elementary charge.

moderator: a material (e.g. graphite) used in a *thermal fission reactor* to slow down the high-speed neutrons produced in the fission reaction, so that they may cause further fissions of uranium nuclei (high-speed neutrons do not cause the fission of uranium-235).

■ The neutrons collide inelastically with graphite nuclei, thus losing some of their kinetic energy.

■ *TIP* Do not confuse the moderator with the *control rods*. Control rods absorb neutrons.

molar gas constant: the constant in the *ideal gas law* equation, given the symbol R.

■ For n mol of an ideal gas having a volume V at pressure p and thermodynamic temperature T, the molar gas constant R is given by

$$R = pV/nT$$

The value of R is $8.31 \, \mathrm{J \, K^{-1} \, mol^{-1}}$. The molar gas constant R is related to the *Boltzmann constant* k and the *Avogadro constant* N_A by the expression

$$k = R/N_A$$

mole: unit of measurement of amount of substance; its abbreviation is mol.

■ One mole of any substance contains a number of molecules (or atoms if the substance is monatomic) equal to the *Avogadro constant*. The mass, measured in grams, of one mole of any substance is numerically equal to the relative molecular/atomic weight of the substance.

■ *e.g.* The molecular weight of nitrogen is 28 and so one mole of nitrogen has mass 28 g.

moment: the turning effect of a force.

■ It is equal to the product of the force and the perpendicular distance of the line of action of the force from the pivot P (fulcrum). In the diagram, the moment of the force about point P = Fd.

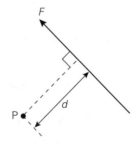

Moment of a force

The SI unit of the moment of a force is newton metre (N m). Moment is a *vector quantity*, being either clockwise or anticlockwise.

■ *e.g.* The *torque* of a *couple* is a moment.

■ *TIP* Do not confuse the unit of moment of a force with that of energy (the joule). Both are the product of a force and a distance. In the case of moment of a force, the force and distance are at right angles. For energy, the force and distance moved are along the same line.

momentum: the product of the mass of an object and its velocity:

momentum = mass × velocity

▧ Since velocity is a *vector quantity*, momentum is also a vector. It is sometimes given the symbol p, and its SI unit is kilogram metre per second (kg m s^{-1}). (See also *Newton's second law of motion; conservation of linear momentum, principle of; force; de Broglie equation*.)

▧ *TIP* A common mistake is to define momentum as 'mass × speed'. Remember that momentum is a vector quantity and must be defined in terms of the velocity of the object.

monochromatic light: light of one wavelength.

▧ Taken literally, monochromatic light means light of one colour; however, colours may have a range of wavelengths, so in physics 'monochromatic' means one wavelength.

▧ *e.g.* *Laser* light is monochromatic.

motor effect: when a current-carrying conductor is at an angle to a magnetic field, or a charged particle moves at an angle to a magnetic field, the conductor or charged particle experiences a force.

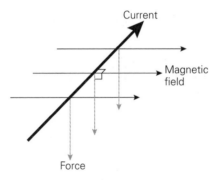

▧ The direction of the force is given by *Fleming's left-hand rule*. For a conductor of length L carrying current I at an angle θ to a magnetic field of flux density B, the force F acting on the conductor is given by

$$F = BIL \sin\theta$$

Similarly, a charge q moving at speed v at an angle θ to a magnetic field of flux density B is given by

$$F = Bqv \sin\theta$$

The equation $F = BIL \sin\theta$ is the basis of the definition of the SI unit of magnetic flux density (the *tesla*, T).

▧ *TIP* When using Fleming's left-hand rule, remember that the second finger points in the direction of conventional current. When predicting the direction

m

of the force on electrons, the second finger points in the opposite direction to the movement of the electrons.

multipath dispersion: the change in shape of a light signal (a pulse) as a result of passing down an *optic fibre.*

▨ Dispersion results from light taking different routes along the fibre. Multipath dispersion is reduced by making the fibre as thin as possible.

nano-: prefix used with a unit to denote the sub-multiple of $\times 10^{-9}$; its symbol is n.

■ *e.g.* 1 nanometre = 1×10^{-9} m = 1 nm. Wavelengths of light are frequently quoted in nanometres.

natural frequency of vibration: the frequency at which an object will vibrate when it is allowed to do so freely (i.e. with no external forces acting on it).

■ *e.g. Resonance* occurs when the natural frequency of a vibrating object is equal to the *forced frequency of vibration*.

neutral equilibrium: an object is in neutral *equilibrium* when it does not return to its original position after it has been displaced slightly; its centre of gravity stays at the same vertical height.

■ *e.g.* When a small ball on a horizontal surface is displaced, it will roll away and come to rest at another position.

■ *TIP* The difference between *unstable equilibrium* and neutral equilibrium is that the centre of gravity falls for unstable equilibrium whereas it stays at the same height when the equilibrium is neutral.

neutron: an uncharged particle with a mass almost equal to that of a proton:

mass of neutron = 1.67×10^{-27} kg

■ Neutrons are found in the nuclei of atoms where, together with protons, they are known as *nucleons*. The neutron is not a fundamental particle but is composed of *quarks*. During beta decay of a nucleus, the number of neutrons in the nucleus decreases by one and the number of protons increases by one. In effect, a neutron has decayed to become a proton and an electron:

$${}^{1}_{0}n \longrightarrow {}^{1}_{1}p + {}^{0}_{-1}e + \text{energy}$$

The reaction is possible because the difference between the mass of a neutron and that of a proton is about twice the mass of an electron. Neutrons may exist outside the nucleus and are then known as 'free' neutrons. Free neutrons are responsible for *nuclear fission*.

neutron diffraction: a technique used for determining crystal structure by *diffraction* of a beam of neutrons.

■ The wavelength of a neutron is related to its speed by the *de Broglie equation*. A neutron with a speed of about $4 \times 10^3 \, \mathrm{m\,s^{-1}}$ will have a wavelength of about $10^{-10} \, \mathrm{m}$. This distance is about the same as the spacing of atoms in a crystal. Neutron diffraction techniques are particularly useful in the study of crystals containing hydrogen atoms. Neutrons are strongly scattered by hydrogen atoms. On the other hand, such atoms scatter X-rays only very weakly. (See also *X-ray diffraction; electron diffraction*.)

neutron-induced fission: see *nuclear fission*.

newton, N: the SI unit of force; it is defined as that force required to give a freely moving body a rate of change of momentum of $1 \, \mathrm{kg\,m\,s^{-2}}$ in the direction of the force.

■ Alternatively, the newton may be defined as that force required to give a mass of 1 kg an acceleration of $1 \, \mathrm{m\,s^{-2}}$ in the direction of the force.

■ *TIP* Since force is a *vector quantity*, when defining the newton it is necessary to state that the change in momentum or the acceleration take place in the direction of the force.

Newton's first law of motion: a body stays at rest or continues to move at constant velocity unless a resultant force acts on it.

■ Note that forces may act on the body when it is at rest or moving with constant velocity. However, under these circumstances, there must be more than one force so that the forces are balanced (i.e. there is no resultant force).

■ *e.g.* An object falling at constant speed through air (its *terminal velocity*) is obeying Newton's first law of motion.

Newton's law of gravitation: the mutual force of attraction between any two point masses is proportional to the product of the masses and inversely proportional to the square of their separation.

■ For two point masses M and m, with separation r, the mutual force F of attraction is given by

$$F = GMm/r^2$$

where G is the *universal constant of gravitation* ($G = 6.67 \times 10^{-11} \, \mathrm{N\,m^2\,kg^{-2}}$).

■ *TIP* When stating the law, you must specify that the masses are point masses. In practice, point masses are not possible, but the law applies to masses whose separation is much greater than their dimensions (separation >> radius).

Newton's laws of motion: three laws which summarise the effects of forces on the motion of bodies.

■ They are the fundamental principles of Newtonian mechanics. (See *Newton's first law of motion; Newton's second law of motion; Newton's third law of motion*.)

Newton's second law of motion: the rate of change of momentum of an object is proportional to the resultant force acting on the object and takes place in the direction of the resultant force.

■ For a change of momentum Δp taking place in time Δt, the resultant force F is given by

$F = \Delta p / \Delta t$

Momentum is the product of mass m and velocity v. If the mass of the object is constant, then

$F = \Delta(mv) / \Delta t = m(\Delta v / \Delta t)$

The term $\Delta v / \Delta t$ is rate of change of velocity, which, by definition, is acceleration a. Thus, for constant mass

$F = ma$

The equations $F = \Delta p / \Delta t$ and $F = ma$ are the equations by which force and its unit, the newton, are defined.

■ *TIP* Be careful to define Newton's second law in terms of rate of change of momentum. Any definition based on $F = ma$ is a simplification in which mass is assumed to be constant. This is not the case in, for example, a rocket.

Newton's third law of motion: whenever a force acts on a body, an equal but oppositely directed force of the same kind acts on another body.

■ Implicit in the law are the assumptions that the forces:

- occur in pairs
- are of the same kind (e.g. magnetic, electric)
- are of equal magnitude
- act along the same line but in opposite directions
- act on different objects

The law of *conservation of momentum* is a direct consequence of Newton's third law.

■ *TIP* The law is frequently summarised as 'action and reaction are equal but opposite'. However, this is rather an over-simplification and should be avoided.

node: a point on a *stationary wave* where the amplitude of vibration is zero or a minimum.

■ The distance between two neighbouring nodes is equal to one half wavelength of the stationary wave.

normal: a line drawn at right-angles to another line or a surface.

■ When referring to reflection or refraction, the normal is a line drawn at right angles to the surface at the point where the incident ray meets the surface.

nuclear equation: an equation using the representation of individual nuclei in order to illustrate a nuclear reaction.

■ In any nuclear equation, *nucleon number*, *proton number* and mass–energy must be conserved.

■ *e.g.* For the alpha decay of radium (Ra) to form radon (Rn), the nuclear equation is

$^{226}_{88}\text{Ra} \longrightarrow {}^{222}_{86}\text{Rn} + {}^{4}_{2}\text{He} + \text{energy}$

- conservation of nucleon number: 226 = 222 + 4

n

- conservation of proton number: $88 = 86 + 2$
- conservation of mass–energy is confirmed using Einstein's equation $E = mc^2$

■ *TIP* An electron is denoted by $_{-1}^{0}e$.

nuclear fission: the splitting of a *nucleus* of high *nucleon number* into two smaller nuclei of approximately equal mass with the release of energy.

■ *e.g.* A nucleus of uranium-235 may be made to undergo fission when bombarded by a neutron (this is known as induced fission).

$$^{235}_{92}U + ^{1}_{0}n \longrightarrow {}^{236}_{92}U \longrightarrow {}^{140}_{54}Xe + {}^{94}_{38}Sr + 2^{1}_{0}n + \gamma + \text{energy}$$

Note that the nuclei produced in this fission reaction are not always $^{140}_{54}Xe$ and $^{94}_{38}Sr$, but we do know that the resulting nuclei will be of approximately the same mass and that either two or three neutrons will be produced. (See also *chain reaction; binding energy; binding energy per nucleon.*)

nuclear fusion: the building up of a larger nucleus from two nuclei of low *nucleon number*, with the release of energy.

■ In general, fusion reactions require very high temperatures and pressures. Research into controlled fusion reactions is being conducted in the UK with what is known as the *JET nuclear fusion project* (Joint European Torus). Deuterium $^{2}_{1}H$ and tritium $^{3}_{1}H$ are used as fuel to produce fusion energy.

$$^{2}_{1}H + ^{3}_{1}H \rightarrow {}^{4}_{2}He + {}^{1}_{0}n + \text{energy}$$

(See also *binding energy, nuclear; binding energy per nucleon.*)

nuclear reactor: see *thermal fission reactor.*

nuclear representation: a short-hand means by which the details of a nucleus may be written down.

■ The element is identified by its chemical symbol; the number of protons in the nucleus is given by the *proton number Z* and the total number of protons and neutrons by the *nucleon number A*. So the general nuclear representation of an element with chemical symbol S is $^{A}_{Z}S$.

■ *e.g.* The nuclear representation of lithium-7 is $^{7}_{3}Li$. This shows that lithium-7 has three protons and four neutrons in its nucleus.

■ *TIP* The proton number also gives the number of extra-nuclear electrons in a neutral atom of the element.

nucleon: the name given to either a proton or a neutron (see also *nucleon number*).

nucleon number (also called 'mass number')**:** the number of nucleons (that is, protons plus neutrons) found in the nucleus of an isotope of an element.

■ Nucleon number is given the symbol A and is one of the two numbers used to represent a nucleus, the other being the *proton number Z*. If the chemical symbol of an element is S, then a nucleus of this element would be represented by $^{A}_{Z}S$.

■ *TIP* The number of neutrons in a nucleus is found by subtracting the nucleon number from the proton number. For example, $^{238}_{92}U$ is a nucleus of uranium, containing 92 protons and 146 neutrons. The proton number also gives the number of electrons orbiting the nucleus of a neutral atom.

n

nucleus: the central core of an atom containing *protons* and *neutrons*.

■ A nucleus has a diameter of about 10^{-14} m (compare that with an atomic diameter of about 10^{-10} m), and contains the majority of the mass of the atom. Nuclear material is very dense (about 10^{14} kg m^{-3}). A nucleus is positively charged. High-energy electron scattering has shown that the radius r of a nucleus having a nucleon number A is given by the expression

$$r = r_0 A^{1/3}$$

where r_0 is the radius of a hydrogen nucleus (about 1.4×10^{-15} m). (See also *nuclear representation*.)

nuclide: a particular species (type) of nucleus that is specified by its proton number and neutron number.

■ *TIP* Do not confuse nuclide with *neutron* or *nucleus* (a neutron is a particle found within a nucleus).

ohm, Ω: the SI unit of *resistance*.

■ The resistance of a *resistor* is given by the word equation

$$\text{resistance (ohms)} = \frac{\text{potential difference (volts)}}{\text{current (amps)}}$$

$$1\ \Omega = 1\ \text{V A}^{-1}$$

■ **TIP** Resistance is calculated by dividing potential difference by the particular value of current it causes; it is not found from the gradient of a graph of voltage against current.

Ohm's law: for a conductor at constant temperature, the current in the conductor is proportional to the potential difference across it:

current $I \propto$ potential difference V

■ Hence, $V = IR$, where R is the *resistance* of the conductor.

■ **TIP** The statement of Ohm's law deals with proportionality — the equation $V = IR$ is effectively the defining equation of resistance, not a statement of Ohm's law.

optic fibre: thin fibre made of very pure glass used for the transmission of light pulses over long distances.

■ Light travels along the optic fibre as a result of *total internal reflection*. The fibre is very thin (a few μm in diameter) to avoid *multipath dispersion*.

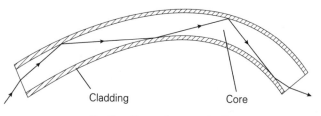

Cladding   Core

Section through an optic fibre

■ **e.g.** In medical diagnosis, optic fibres are used in endoscopes to illuminate and view the interior of the body.

O

■ *TIP* It is not only light that can be transmitted through optic fibres; in optical communication, for example, infrared radiation is usually used.

oscillation: a to-and-fro movement of a particle about a fixed point.

■ The particle moves away from the fixed point, slows down and stops, then returns to the point, overshoots and slows down. It then reverses its direction of motion, returning to the fixed point. The complete motion is then repeated.

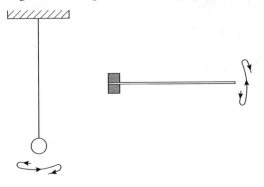

An oscillation about a fixed point

■ *e.g.* Oscillations of a *simple pendulum* bob; oscillations of a point in a *wave*.

parallax error: a random error (*uncertainty*) brought about by not looking at right-angles to a scale when the scale reading is being taken.

■ *TIP* Parallax errors should be minimised by placing a plane mirror behind the scale or using a set-square.

parent nucleus: a term used in nuclear physics to indicate a nucleus which is transformed with the emission of particles and/or energy to form another nucleus (the *daughter nucleus*):

parent nucleus → daughter nucleus + particles and/or energy

parsec, pc: a unit of measurement of distance in astronomy.

■ It is defined as the distance at which one *astronomical unit* (1 AU) perpendicular to the observer's line of sight subtends an angle of one arc second:

1 parsec = 3.09×10^{16} m = 3.26 *light-years*

Astronomical distances are so large that the megaparsec (Mpc) is often used.

pascal, Pa: the SI unit for the measurement of *pressure* or tensile *stress*.

■ One pascal is equal to one newton per metre squared ($N\,m^{-2}$), the force being normal to the area. The base unit of the pascal is $kg\,m^{-1}\,s^{-2}$.

path difference: the extra distance that one wave travels compared with another wave.

■ This path difference is usually expressed in terms of the wavelength of the two waves. Path difference gives rise to a phase difference between waves. For two waves initially in phase and of wavelength λ, a path difference x can be expressed as

path difference = x/λ wavelengths

phase difference = $2\pi(x/\lambda)$ rad = $360(x/\lambda)$ degrees

Path difference is often the quantity that is used when explaining an interference pattern. (See also *two-source interference; diffraction grating*.)

pd: see *potential difference*.

peak value: see *alternating current or voltage*.

pendulum: see *simple pendulum*.

penetrating power: see *attenuation*.

period: the time taken to complete one *oscillation* in a vibrating system.

■ For a particle undergoing simple harmonic motion, the period T may be shown on a displacement–time graph. The SI unit of period is the second (s).

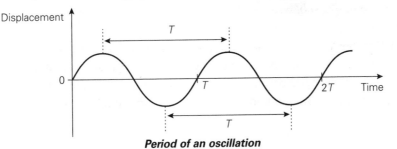

Period of an oscillation

It can be seen from the graph that period may be defined as the time elapsed between successive occasions when a particle is moving through the same point in the same direction. Period of oscillation T (in seconds) is related to *frequency* (in *hertz*) by the expression

$$T = 1/f$$

permeability of free space: a constant relating magnetic flux density B at a point to current in a wire or coil when in a vacuum.

■ The permeability of free space is given the symbol μ_0 and its SI unit is henry per metre ($H\,m^{-1}$).

$$\mu_0 = 4\pi \times 10^{-7}\ H\,m^{-1}$$

For a current I, the magnetic flux density B is given by the following equations:

● at distance r from a long straight wire: $B = \mu_0 I/2\pi r$

● at the centre of a flat coil of radius r having N turns: $B = \mu_0 NI/2r$

● along the axis of a long solenoid having n turns per unit length: $B = \mu_0 nI$.

■ *TIP* It is quite likely that you are not familiar with the unit of μ_0: the henry is a unit associated with electromagnetic induction that is beyond most AS/A-level specifications.

permittivity of free space: the constant ε_0 in the formula representing *Coulomb's law*, namely

$$F = Q_1 Q_2/4\pi\varepsilon_0 r^2$$

■ The constant has the value $8.85 \times 10^{-12}\ F\,m^{-1}$ (farad per metre).

■ *TIP* It is sometimes useful to remember that $1/4\pi\varepsilon_0 \approx 9 \times 10^9$, but be careful because this result is to one significant figure, and data for many calculations are given to either two or three significant figures.

peta-: prefix used with a unit to denote the multiple of $\times\ 10^{15}$; its symbol is P.

■ *e.g.* 1 petametre $= 1 \times 10^{15}\,m = 1\,Pm$.

phase: an angle in either degrees (°) or radians (rad) which gives a measure of the fraction of a cycle that has been completed by an oscillating particle or by a wave.

■ One oscillation or cycle corresponds to 360° or 2π rad. For a phase angle ϕ, the fraction of the oscillation or cycle that has been completed is given by

fraction = $\phi/2\pi$, where ϕ is in rad

fraction = $\phi/360$, where ϕ is in degrees

(See also *phase difference*.)

phase difference: a measure of how much one wave is out of step with another.

■ Phase difference is measured in either degrees (°) or radians (rad). A phase difference of one cycle corresponds to 360° or 2π rad. It is important to state whether the wave in question leads or lags behind the reference wave.

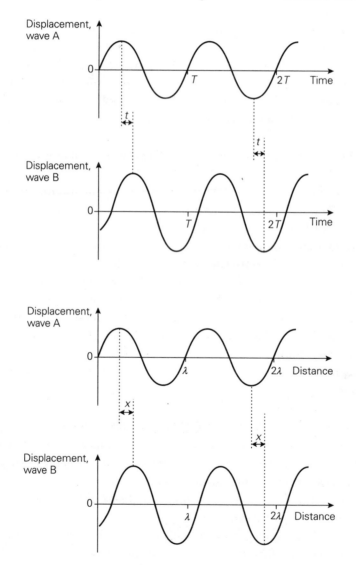

Determination of phase angle

In the diagram, wave A leads wave B by the phase angle ϕ given by

ϕ (rad) $= 2\pi(t/T)$ or $2\pi(x/\lambda)$

ϕ (°) $= 360(t/T)$ or $360(x/\lambda)$

'In phase' implies a phase angle of zero. 'Out of phase' refers to a phase angle that is not zero. Antiphase is the term used for a phase difference of 180° or π rad. (See also *interference*.)

■ *TIP* Do not confuse 'lead' and 'lag'. In the diagram, it may be thought that wave A lags behind wave B because the crests of wave A are further to the left than those of wave B. However, 'time' is plotted on the x-axis, so further left means an earlier time and hence a lead.

photoelectric effect: the ejection of an electron from a metal surface when the surface is irradiated with *electromagnetic radiation* of a high enough frequency.

■ The lowest frequency that gives rise to the ejection of electrons from a particular surface is known as the *threshold frequency*. For many metals, this frequency lies in the ultraviolet region of the electromagnetic spectrum, but for the alkali metals, it lies within the visible region. The following observations are made for the photoelectric effect:

- the photoelectric effect is not observed for frequencies less than the threshold frequency for that surface
- the maximum kinetic energy of a photoelectron depends on the frequency of the incident radiation and not on the intensity of the radiation
- at constant frequency, the rate of ejection of electrons increases with increase of intensity of the incident radiation
- the ejection of an electron occurs within a very short time of the arrival of the radiation (less than 1 ns)

These observations cannot be explained on the basis of a wave nature for electromagnetic radiation and gave rise to the concept of a *photon* as a particle of electromagnetic radiation. The kinetic energy of a photoelectron is related to the threshold frequency and other factors by the *photoelectric effect equation*.

photoelectric effect equation: a statement of the law of *conservation of energy*, related to the *photoelectric effect*.

■ For a *photon* of light incident on a metal surface, some of the photon energy will be used to provide the *work function energy* (the energy required to eject an electron from the surface) and, for an electron at the surface of the metal, the remainder of the energy will be seen as kinetic energy. This kinetic energy is a maximum. The photoelectric equation can be written as

$$\begin{array}{ccc} \text{photon} \\ \text{energy} \end{array} = \begin{array}{c} \text{work function} \\ \text{energy} \end{array} + \begin{array}{c} \text{maximum kinetic} \\ \text{energy of electron} \end{array}$$

$$hf = hf_0 + \left(\tfrac{1}{2}mv^2\right)_{max}$$

where f is the frequency of the incident radiation, f_0 is the *threshold frequency*, *h* is the *Planck constant* and $(\frac{1}{2}mv^2)_{max}$ is the maximum kinetic energy of an emitted electron. The product hf_0 is equal to the work function energy. Electrons below the surface would require energy to bring them to the surface and thus would have less kinetic energy.

■ *e.g.* The photoelectric effect provides a simple means by which the Planck constant *h* may be determined.

photon: a quantum of electromagnetic energy.

■ Each quantum or 'packet' is a discrete quantity of energy, dependent only on the frequency of the radiation. Photon energy *E* is related to frequency *f* by the expression

$$E = hf$$

where *h* is the *Planck constant*. Since frequency is related to wavelength λ and the speed *c* of light in a vacuum by the expression $c = f\lambda$, it follows that

$$E = hf = hc/\lambda$$

■ *TIP* Increasing the intensity of a beam of electromagnetic radiation of one frequency means that the rate of arrival of photons has increased. Each photon still has the same energy; however, where the frequency of the radiation increases but the intensity remains constant, the photon energy will increase and the rate of arrival of photons will decrease.

pico-: prefix used with a unit to denote the sub-multiple of $\times 10^{-12}$; its symbol is p.

e.g. 1 picofarad = 1×10^{-12} F = 1 pF. Small-value capacitances are often quoted in picofarads.

pitch: the subjective perception of the *frequency* of sound.

■ Pitch is often thought to be the same as frequency but, more precisely, it is what we hear when frequency is interpreted by our ears and brain. That is, it is the response of the ear to a particular frequency of sound.

Planck constant: a value that relates the energy of a *photon* to its frequency *f*; its symbol is *h*.

■ The energy *E* is given by

$$E = hf$$

The Planck constant has the value 6.63×10^{-34} J s.

plasma: the fourth state of matter, consisting of free electrons and atoms from which the electrons have been stripped.

■ A plasma exists only at very high temperatures. The thermal energy is so great that electrons have broken free of the nuclear attraction, giving rise to free electrons and positive ions moving randomly at very high speeds.

■ *e.g.* Plasma is important in nuclear reactions in the sun and in the *JET nuclear fusion project*.

■ *TIP* Plasma physics is not studied at AS/A-level; however, you should be aware of the existence of a plasma in order to understand nuclear fusion reactions.

plastic deformation: a permanent change in shape or size of a sample of material when the sample has been under *stress*.

■ The material undergoes a change in internal structure.

plasticity: the tendency of an object or a sample of material to retain any change in shape or size when any deforming forces are removed from it.

■ Plasticity is the opposite of *elasticity*.

Poiseuille's equation: an equation that gives the volume flow rate of fluid through a cylindrical pipe.

■ For a pipe of radius r and length l

$$\text{volume flow rate} = (\pi/8\eta)r^4(p/l)$$

where p is the pressure difference between the ends of the pipe and η is the *coefficient of viscosity* of the fluid. Note that the fluid flow must be streamline. The dependence of flow rate on the fourth power of the radius shows the crucial role of radius on flow rate.

polarisation: where the oscillations in a wave are confined to one direction only, the direction being at right angles to the direction of propagation of the wave.

■ Only transverse waves may be polarised. *Polaroid* sheets may be used to polarise a beam of light (*electromagnetic radiation*). A Polaroid sheet allows the electric vector in one direction only to be transmitted. This direction is referred to as the direction of polarisation. When a second sheet of Polaroid (called 'the analyser') is introduced behind the first sheet (called the 'polariser') and rotated, the intensity of transmitted light is reduced, becoming zero at the point where the direction of polarisation of the two Polaroid sheets are at right angles (the Polaroid sheets are said to be 'crossed').

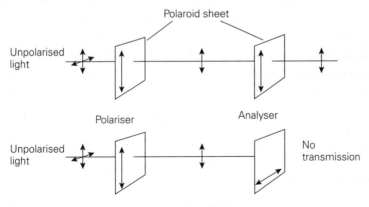

Polarisation of light

Microwaves may be polarised using a metal grid. The electric vector parallel to the lines of the grid is absorbed.

■ *e.g.* Light is polarised on reflection from a surface — hence the use of Polaroid sunglasses to reduce glare.

■ *TIP* It is a common misunderstanding that a diffraction grating produces polarised light — with the lines of the grating acting as a polariser — this is not so. Remember that polarisation is a phenomenon associated with transverse waves only.

Polaroid: a manufacturer's name for sheets of a nitrocellulose material covered with crystals of quinine iodosulphate that polarises light.

■ All the crystals are lined up and the electric vector of the light (an *electromagnetic wave*) in the direction of the crystals causes electrons in the crystals to vibrate, thus absorbing the energy associated with that vector. The electric vector normal to the direction of alignment of the crystals is transmitted.

polymeric material (also called 'polymer'): a material consisting of molecules comprising long chains of atoms.

■ Such materials are capable of large *strains* without breaking. Different values of strain are obtained on increasing and then decreasing the *stress*.

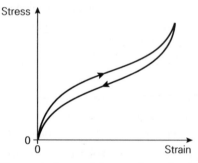

Stress–strain graph for a polymeric material

■ *e.g.* Rubber is a polymeric material and has a breaking strain of around 5 (compare this with copper, which has a breaking strain of about 0.05).

positron: one of the fundamental particles, having the same mass as an electron but with a positive charge equal in magnitude to that of the electron.

potential difference (pd): the energy per unit charge transferred from electrical energy to some other form when charge passes through an electrical component:

$$\text{potential difference } V = \frac{\text{energy transferred } W}{\text{charge } Q}$$

■ The potential difference is measured across the component. The SI unit of potential difference is joule per coulomb ($J\,C^{-1}$) or volt (V).

■ *TIP* Remember that the energy transfer is from electrical to some other form. This is important when distinguishing between potential difference and *electromotive force*.

potential divider: two resistors connected in series with a supply voltage.

■ The *potential difference* (pd) across each of the two resistors is less than the *electromotive force* (emf) of the supply.

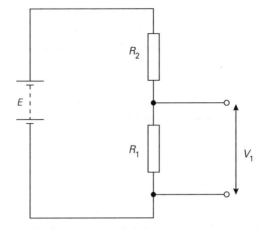

For the circuit shown in the diagram

$$\frac{\text{pd across } R_1}{\text{emf of supply}} = \frac{V_1}{E} = \frac{R_1}{R_1 + R_2}$$

If the resistor R_2 is replaced with a *thermistor*, a *light-dependent resistor* or a *strain gauge*, the output voltage across R_1 is dependent on temperature, light intensity or strain, respectively.

■ **e.g.** One type of potential divider is a potentiometer.

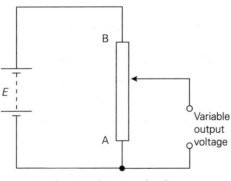

A potentiometer circuit

A variable direct voltage may be obtained from a fixed supply voltage. Moving the sliding contact from A to B in the circuit illustrated increases the output from zero to E.

■ ***TIP*** Remember that, in the diagram of the potential divider, as the resistance of R_2 increases, the voltage across R_1 decreases.

potential gradient: the rate of change of electric potential with distance; its SI unit is volt per metre ($V\,m^{-1}$).

■ For parallel conducting plates whose dimensions are large compared with their separation, the electric field between the plates is as shown in the diagram.

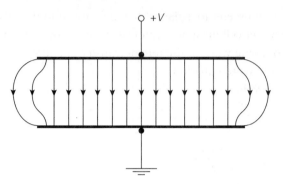

Electric field between parallel plates

Over the majority of the space between the plates, the electric field lines are parallel and equally spaced and thus the electric field is uniform. For two such plates, separated by distance d and with a potential difference V between them, the electric field E between the plates is given by

$E = V/d$ (the potential gradient)

■ *TIP* In many calculations, the 'edge effect' where the field is non-uniform is neglected.

potentiometer: see *potential divider.*

potentiometer, slide-wire: a device used for the comparison of *potential differences* or *electromotive forces.*

■ It consists of a uniform homogeneous wire connected to a battery (driver cell). The potential difference along the wire is proportional to the length of wire, provided the current in the wire is constant. With the cell of emf E_1 connected as shown in the diagram, the galvanometer (milliammeter) shows no deflection when the sliding contact (jockey) is at X and PX = L_1. For a second cell of emf E_2, the length PX for which there will be no current in the galvanometer is L_2. Then

$E_1/E_2 = L_1/L_2$

Driver cell

L_1

P

X

Uniform wire

Sliding contact (jockey)

E_1

A slide-wire potentiometer

▓ *TIP* For the potentiometer to 'balance' (i.e. no current in the galvanometer), the emf of the driver cell must be greater than that of the cell under test.

power: the rate of doing work or the rate of transfer of energy.

▓ It is defined by the word equation

$$\text{power} = \frac{\text{work done}}{\text{time taken}}$$

or

$$\text{power} = \frac{\text{energy transferred}}{\text{time taken}}$$

Power is a scalar quantity and, in the SI system, is measured in watts (W) where $1\,\text{W} = 1\,\text{J s}^{-1}$. Since *work* is the product of *force F* and *displacement x*, if this work is done in time t, then

power = Fx/t

But x/t is *velocity v*, and hence

power = Fv

Note that v is the velocity in the direction of the force. *Electric power P* is related to potential difference V and current I by the expression

$P = VI$

power of a lens: the reciprocal of the focal length of a lens, when the focal length is measured in metres.

▓ The unit of lens power is the dioptre (D) or m^{-1}. Thus, a diverging lens of focal length 25 cm has focal length $f = -0.25\,\text{m}$ and power $-4.0\,\text{D}$. For a combination of lenses in contact, the total power is found by addition of the individual powers.

▓ *TIP* Remember to apply the sign convention (see *lens formula* for more information).

precision: a term used to describe the level of *uncertainty* in an instrument's scale.

▓ A metre rule will have a precision of ±1 mm, whereas a micrometer screw gauge is precise to ±0.01 mm. Many instruments have a precision that exceeds their *accuracy*. Although a digital voltmeter may have a precision of ±0.01 V, its reading may differ from the true value by 0.1 V.

▓ *TIP* Do not confuse precision with accuracy. An instrument may be precise (i.e. have small scale divisions) but still be inaccurate (give readings far from the true values).

prefix: used with *SI system* units to indicate a multiple or a sub-multiple of the quantity.

▓ Each prefix has a symbol which is written in front of the unit symbol.

▓ *e.g.* The prefix milli- indicates one-thousandth ($\times 10^{-3}$) and has the symbol m. A millimetre (mm) is one-thousandth of a metre.

Prefix		Symbol
peta	$\times 10^{15}$	P
tera	$\times 10^{12}$	T
giga	$\times 10^{9}$	G
mega	$\times 10^{6}$	M
kilo	$\times 10^{3}$	k
centi	$\times 10^{-2}$	c
milli	$\times 10^{-3}$	m
micro	$\times 10^{-6}$	μ
nano	$\times 10^{-9}$	n
pico	$\times 10^{-12}$	p
femto	$\times 10^{-15}$	f

■ *TIP* Note that all prefixes indicating a multiple of the quantity are capital letters, except for kilo (k), while those indicating a sub-multiple are lower-case letters. When writing down the prefix to a unit, do not leave a space between the prefix and the unit: Tm means terametres but T m means tesla metres!

pressure: force per unit area, where the force is acting at right angles to the area.

■ For a force F acting normally on area A, the pressure p is given by

$$p = F/A$$

The SI unit of pressure is the pascal (Pa), which is equal to 1 newton per metre squared (1 Pa = 1 N m^{-2}).

■ *e.g.* Pressure in a fluid and pressure of an ideal gas.

■ *TIP* Do not define pressure as the force acting at right angles to a unit area. The ratio of force to area must be made clear. Also remember that pressure is defined in terms of a force normal to an area.

pressure in a fluid: pressure in a fluid acts in all directions and is transmitted through the fluid; it is a *scalar quantity.*

■ For an incompressible liquid of *density* ρ (in kg m^{-3}), the pressure p (in Pa) at depth h (in m) in the liquid is given by the equation

$$p = \rho g h$$

where g is the *acceleration of free fall*. This formula does not apply directly to gases because, since gases can be compressed easily, their density increases with depth. The pressure in the Earth's atmosphere varies exponentially (approximately) with depth.

pressure law: the pressure of a fixed mass of gas at constant volume is proportional to its thermodynamic temperature.

■ For a mass of gas having pressure p_1 at thermodynamic temperature T_1 and pressure p_2 at temperature T_2, with the volume remaining constant,

$$p \propto T \text{ and } p/T = \text{constant}$$

We can also say that

$$p_1/T_1 = p_2/T_2 = \text{constant}$$

The law was discovered by experiment and is largely the work of Gay Lussac. The law applies to all gases as long as they are at a sufficiently high temperature — the actual temperature being dependent on the gas itself. The pressure law applies to oxygen and nitrogen at room temperature but not to carbon dioxide. The history of the experimental discovery is complicated by the development of temperature scales. The original work was not done in terms of thermo-dynamic temperature. (See also *ideal gas law*.)

■ *TIP* Remember that the law applies to a fixed mass of gas at constant volume.

pressure of an ideal gas: pressure that is related to the *mean square speed* $<c^2>$ of the molecules by the expression

$$\text{pressure } p = \tfrac{1}{3}\rho <c^2>$$

where ρ is the density of the gas.

■ If the number of molecules per unit volume is n and each molecule has mass m, then

$$p = \tfrac{1}{3}\rho <c^2> = \tfrac{1}{3}nm <c^2>$$

The importance of these equations is that they link properties of individual molecules (e.g. mean square speed) to a property of the whole gas (i.e. pressure). (See also *kinetic theory of gases*.)

principal axis: a line drawn at right angles to the plane of a lens through its centre.

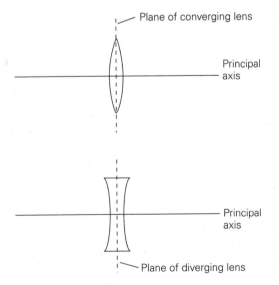

Principal axis of a lens

■ *e.g.* It gives the initial direction of light when defining *principal focus*.

p

principal focus (also called 'focal point'): the point to which rays of light, initially parallel and close to the *principal axis*, converge (or from which they appear to diverge) after passing through a lens.

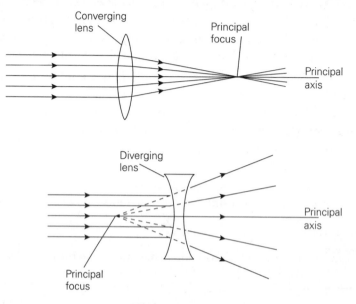

Principal focus of a lens

▨ The distance from the centre of the lens to the principal focus is known as the focal length of the lens. (See also *lens formula*.)

principle of moments: for a body to be in *equilibrium*, the sum of all the clockwise *moments* about any point must equal the sum of all the anticlockwise moments about that same point.

▨ **TIP** Remember that a statement of the principle of moments is only one of the two conditions that must be fulfilled for a body to be in equilibrium (the other being that the algebraic sum of the *forces* acting on the object in any direction must be zero). When solving problems using this principle, it is often helpful to write down a word equation listing all moments before substituting values. Taking moments about a point through which a force acts means that the moment of that force about the point is zero; the force does not enter into the equation for moments about that point.

principle of superposition: when two waves meet at a point, the resultant *displacement* is equal to the vector sum of the individual displacements.

▨ The two waves must be of the same type (sound, electromagnetic, etc.) and, if they are *transverse waves*, the direction of their *polarisation* must be the same.

▨ **e.g.** The principle can be used to explain the formation of *stationary waves* and *interference* patterns.

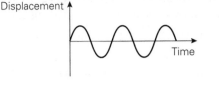

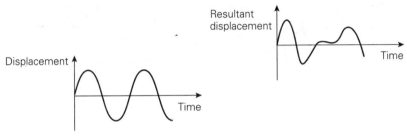

Superposition

■ **TIP** Do not confuse superposition with constructive or destructive interference. The principle of superposition is a statement of how two waves combine.

progressive wave: a wave in which energy is carried from one point to another by means of vibrations or oscillations within the wave.

■ Particles within the wave are not transported along the wave. In a progressive wave, neighbouring particles vibrate with the same amplitude but are out of phase.

■ **e.g.** *Sound waves* and *electromagnetic waves* are both progressive waves.

■ **TIP** You may be asked to compare the properties of *stationary waves* and progressive waves. If so, you must include in your discussion energy transfer and the phase and amplitude of vibration of particles.

projectile motion: the resultant motion of an object when it is free to move in both the horizontal and vertical directions.

■ When analysing the motion of a projectile, the horizontal motion is treated independently of the vertical motion so that the *equations of motion* can be applied. Assuming that air resistance may be neglected, the object will continue with constant speed in the horizontal direction. In the vertical direction, the object will have the acceleration of free fall.

■ **TIP** If an object is projected upwards from ground level, the time to return to ground level is twice the time to reach maximum height. At maximum height, the vertical velocity is zero.

proton: a particle having a positive charge equal in magnitude to the charge on an electron and a mass approximately equal to that of a neutron:

$$\text{charge on proton} = +1.6 \times 10^{-19}\,\text{C}$$
$$\text{mass of proton} = 1.67 \times 10^{-27}\,\text{kg}$$

■ Protons and neutrons are collectively referred to as *nucleons*. A proton is not a fundamental particle but is composed of *quarks*. The lightest isotope of hydrogen has a single proton as its nucleus.

proton number (also called 'atomic number'): the number of protons found in the nucleus of an atom.

■ Proton number is given the symbol Z and is one of the two numbers used to represent a nucleus, the other being the *nucleon number A*. If the chemical symbol of an element is S, then a nucleus of this element would be represented by ^A_ZS.

■ *TIP* The proton number also gives the number of electrons orbiting the nucleus of a neutral atom.

quantisation of charge: a term referring to the fact that charge is not a continuously variable quantity.

- The smallest change in charge is known as the *elementary charge*, and has the magnitude of the charge on an electron. (See also *Millikan's oil drop experiment*.)

quantum: see *photon; Planck constant.*

quark: a fundamental particle that cannot exist separately but only in pairs or triplets.

- Six different quarks, and their corresponding antiquarks, have been identified. Of importance in AS/A-level physics are the up-quark, which has a charge of $+\frac{2}{3}e$, and the down-quark, which has a charge of $-\frac{1}{3}e$.

- *e.g.* A *proton* is composed of two up-quarks and one down-quark. A *neutron* consists of one up-quark and two down-quarks. (See also *baryon; meson.*)

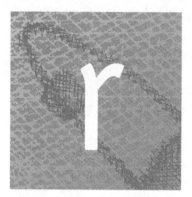

radial field: a field of force in which the field lines either diverge from a point or converge to a point.

■ The field becomes progressively weaker with increasing distance from the point.

■ *e.g.* The electric field due to a point charge and the gravitational field due to a point mass are examples of radial fields.

radian, rad: a unit for the measurement of angle.

■ One radian is that angle subtended at the centre of a circle by an arc equal in length to the radius.

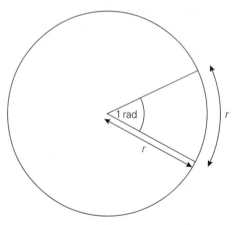

Radian measure

Since the circumference of a circle is of length $2\pi r$, then there are $2\pi r/r = 2\pi$ rad in one revolution and $360° = 2\pi$ rad.

radioactive decay (also called 'radioactivity'): the spontaneous decay of a nucleus with the emission of an alpha particle or a beta particle, and usually accompanied by the emission of a gamma ray photon.

■ The radioactive material contains unstable nuclei that decay to form an isotope of another element. Gamma ray photons are emitted so that the new nucleus is not in an excited energy state. The new nucleus may, itself, be radioactive.

▦ *e.g.* Alpha decay, beta decay (see also *half-life*; *radioactive decay constant*).

▦ *TIP* The isotope emitting the alpha particle or beta particle and/or gamma ray photon is radioactive; the emissions themselves are not radioactive.

radioactive decay constant: the probability of decay per unit time of a nucleus.

▦ The decay constant is fundamental to the understanding of radioactive decay in that the process is spontaneous and random. The decay constant expresses this randomness. If, in a sample of N nuclei of a radioactive isotope, dN nuclei decay in a time dt, then the probability of decay is $-dN/N$. (The minus sign is necessary because the number of nuclei is decreasing.) The probability of decay per unit time is given by

$(-dN/N)/dt$

and this is equal to the decay constant λ. Hence,

$\lambda = (-dN/N)/dt$

Re-arranging gives

$dN/N = -\lambda dt$

The solution of this equation is an exponential function and is given by

$N = N_0 \, e^{-\lambda t}$

This equation is the *radioactive decay equation*. The equation

$\lambda = (-dN/N)/dt$

may be re-arranged in the form

$dN/dt = -\lambda N$

Since dN/dt is the rate of decay of the nuclei, that is, the *activity* of the sample, the activity A is related to the number N of nuclei present by the expression

$A = -\lambda N$

The decay constant λ is related to the *half-life* $t_{\frac{1}{2}}$ of the radioactive isotope by the expression

$\lambda t_{\frac{1}{2}} = \ln 2 \approx 0.693$

▦ *TIP* Although the decay constant is related directly to what is meant by the randomness of radioactive decay, the decay constant cannot be measured directly. Instead, half-life is determined and then the decay constant is calculated from this.

radioactive decay equation: an equation that relates the number N of radioactive nuclei remaining after time t to the initial number N_0:

$N = N_0 e^{-\lambda t} = N_0 \exp(-\lambda t)$

▦ Since the *activity* A of the sample is related to the number of nuclei present by the expression

$A = -\lambda N$

then
$$A = A_0 e^{-\lambda t} = A_0 \exp(-\lambda t)$$

where A_0 is the initial activity (i.e. at time $t = 0$). The equations may also be written in terms of *half-life* $t_{\frac{1}{2}}$, since $\lambda t_{\frac{1}{2}} = \ln 2$, and so
$$N = N_0 \exp(-t \ln 2/t_{\frac{1}{2}})$$

and
$$A = A_0 \exp(-t \ln 2/t_{\frac{1}{2}})$$

radioactivity: see *radioactive decay.*

radio waves: *electromagnetic waves* with wavelengths that are longer than about 10 cm.

■ They are produced by accelerating (oscillating) electrons.

■ *e.g.* Radio waves are used for communication. They are also emitted by some astronomical bodies.

random error: see *uncertainty.*

random motion: the erratic and unpredictable motion of an atom or molecule in a liquid or a gas.

■ Neither the speed nor the direction of a particular atom or molecule can be predicted. The atom or molecule repeatedly changes speed and direction as a result of collisions with other atoms or molecules or the walls of the container.

■ *e.g. Brownian motion* of small particles in a fluid results from the random motion of molecules of the fluid.

randomness: a term used to describe the nature of *radioactive decay.*

■ In any sample of a radioactive material, it is not possible to predict which nucleus will decay next and thus the decays appear randomly throughout the sample. Although the decays in the sample may be random, any nucleus has a constant probability of decay per unit time, referred to as the *decay constant.*

■ *TIP* Do not confuse randomness with *spontaneity.*

rarefaction: a region in a medium where the pressure is below average.

■ Rarefactions are often associated with sound waves where a series of rarefactions and *compressions* move outwards from a sound source, carrying wave energy.

■ *e.g.* A *longitudinal wave* is made up of a series of rarefactions and *compressions.*

ray: the direction in which the energy of a wave is travelling.

■ Rays are drawn at right angles to *wavefronts.*

■ *TIP* Do not forget that a ray has a direction and hence arrowheads should be drawn on rays.

rectification: the means by which alternating current is converted into direct current.

■ Half-wave rectification may be achieved using the circuit shown in diagram (a) below.

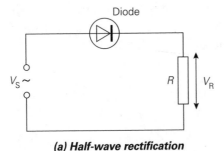

(a) Half-wave rectification

Assuming that the diode is ideal (it has infinite resistance in one direction and a small finite resistance in the other), the supply voltage V_S and the voltage across the resistor V_R will be as shown in (b).

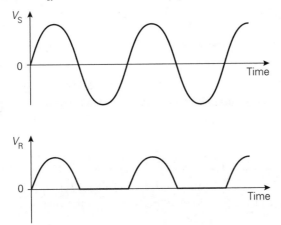

(b) Output voltage for half-wave rectification

Note that rectification means that the current or voltage is in one direction only; it does not mean a constant current or voltage. Full-wave rectification is achieved using a bridge rectifier as shown in (c).

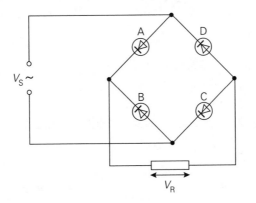

(c) Full-wave rectification

117

Diodes A and C conduct during one half of the cycle of the alternating supply and diodes B and D in the other. The voltage V_R across the resistor and the supply voltage V_S are shown in (d).

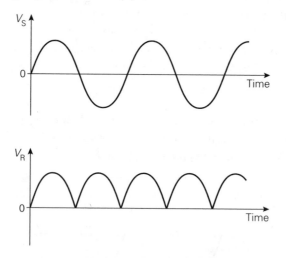

(d) Output voltage for full-wave rectification

Note that the output is in one direction but is not constant. The variation in the output is reduced using *smoothing*.

■ *TIP* It is useful to remember that all the diodes 'point' from one end of the output resistor towards the other end. Remember too that the supply voltage may not be appropriate for the rectifier — if this is the case, then a *transformer* is required.

red shift: see *Doppler shift.*

reflecting prisms: prisms used to reflect light using *total internal reflection.*

■ The *critical angle* for a glass–air boundary is about 42° and thus, for an angle greater than this, the rays are reflected.

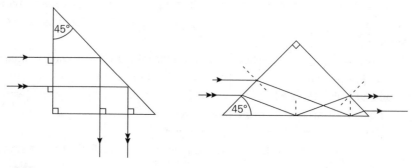

Reflection through 90°　　　　　　**Inverting prism**

Such prisms reflect light without giving rise to multiple images.

reflection: the change in direction of a wave at the surface of a medium such that the wave stays in the same medium. The change in direction is governed by the laws of reflection (see *reflection of light, laws of*). Reflection is not confined to light: it is a phenomenon associated with all waves.

■ *TIP* Reflection differs from refraction in that, for reflection, the wave stays in the same medium. For refraction, the wave changes medium.

reflection of light, laws of: laws governing the change in direction of a wave when it is reflected at a surface.

■ The laws are:
- The incident ray, the reflected ray and the normal all lie in the same plane
- The angle of incidence is equal to the angle of reflection

In effect, the first law states that reflection is a phenomenon that may be fully represented by a diagram drawn on a flat piece of paper. That is, it is a two-dimensional phenomenon. The second law enables the reflected ray to be traced.

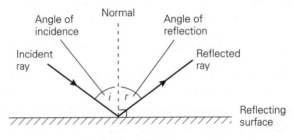

Reflection of a wave

■ *TIP* Always draw in the normal and practise using a protractor!

refraction: the change in direction (bending) of a wave as it passes from one medium to another.

■ The extent of the bending depends on the *refractive index* between the two media and is governed by the laws of refraction (see *refraction of light, laws of*). Refraction is not confined to light: it is a phenomenon associated with all waves. It occurs as a result of a change of speed of the wave between the two media.

■ *TIP* Refraction differs from reflection in that, for refraction, the wave changes medium. For reflection, the wave stays in the same medium.

refraction of light, laws of: laws governing the change in direction of a wave when it passes from one medium to another.

■ The laws are:
- the incident ray, the refracted ray and the normal all lie in the same plane
- the sine of the angle of incidence divided by the sine of the angle of refraction is a constant for any two media

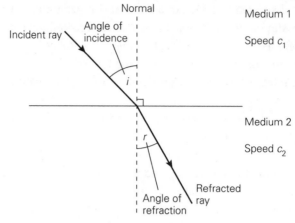

Refraction of light

The first law is similar to the first law of reflection and tells us that refraction is a two-dimensional phenomenon that can be fully represented on a flat piece of paper. The second law enables the direction of the refracted ray to be determined.

$$\sin i / \sin r = n$$

where n is a constant for the wave passing from one medium to another and is known as the *refractive index*. Refraction is a result of a change in speed of the wave as it travels from one medium to another. Refractive index is related to the speeds by the equation

$$n = c_1/c_2 = \sin i / \sin r$$

Note that, if the wave passes from medium 2 to medium 1, the refractive index $_2n_1$ is related to the refractive index $_1n_2$ for the wave passing from medium 1 to medium 2 by the expression

$$_2n_1 = 1/_1n_2$$

■ *e.g.* The refractive index for light travelling from air to glass is about $\frac{3}{2}$ and for light travelling from air to water about $\frac{4}{3}$.

refractive index: a property defined using the laws of refraction (see *refraction of light, laws of*).

■ Consider a wave travelling across a boundary between two media. The speed of the wave in medium 1 is c_1 and in medium 2 is c_2.

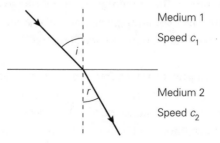

In medium 1, the angle of incidence is i, and in medium 2 the angle of refraction is r. The refractive index $_1n_2$ for the wave travelling from medium 1 to medium 2 is

$_1n_2 = \sin i/\sin r = c_1/c_2$

The refractive index $_2n_1$ when travelling from medium 2 to medium 1 is related to $_1n_2$ by the expression

$_2n_1 = 1/_1n_2$

■ *e.g.* Refractive index is the basis for the understanding of *critical angle, total internal reflection, reflecting prisms* and *optic fibres*.

resistance, electrical: the ratio of the *potential difference V* across a component to the current I through it.

resistance $R = V/I$

Resistance is measured in *ohm* (Ω). For most electrical components, resistance changes with temperature. In the region of room temperature, metals generally show a slight increase of resistance with temperature rise. (See also *light-dependent resistor; thermistor.*)

■ *e.g.* *Resistors* are said to have resistance.

■ *TIP* Resistance is calculated by dividing a specific value of potential difference by the corresponding value of current. It is not determined from the gradient of the current–voltage characteristic.

resistivity: a relationship between the dimensions of a specimen of a material and its resistance that is constant at constant temperature.

■ For a sample of length L, with a uniform cross-sectional area A and resistance R, the resistivity ρ is given by

$\rho = (RA)/L$

The unit of resistivity is ohm metre ($\Omega\,m$).

■ *TIP* When defining resistivity, it is best either to give a word equation or to give the equation in symbols and then to explain the symbols. Remember that A is cross-sectional area, not merely 'area'. Also, be careful with the unit — it is not $\Omega\,m^{-1}$.

resistor: an electrical component that limits the size of the current in a circuit.

■ The value of the *resistance* of the resistor is measured in ohms (Ω). A resistor is characterised by the fact that *electrical energy* is dissipated in it. *Charge carriers* migrate through the resistor, colliding with atoms or molecules of the material and thus increasing the amplitude of vibration of the atoms or molecules. Some of the energy of the charge carriers is transferred to the vibrating atoms or molecules.

■ *e.g.* *Thermistors* and *light-dependent resistors*.

resistors in parallel: a number of resistors connected such that the total current is shared between all of the resistors.

■ The terminals of each individual resistor are connected to the same two points.

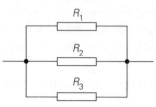

The combined resistance R of resistors of resistances R_1, R_2, R_3, etc., connected in parallel is given by

$$1/R = 1/R_1 + 1/R_2 + 1/R_3 + \ldots$$

It is important to note that the combined resistance is less than the smallest resistance.

■ *TIP* A common mistake is to fail to take the reciprocal when finding the final answer. Check that your answer is less than the smallest resistance.

resistors in series: a number of resistors connected such that the same current passes through all of them.

■ The resistors are connected end to end.

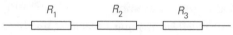

The combined resistance R of resistors of resistances R_1, R_2, R_3, etc., connected in series is given by

$$R = R_1 + R_2 + R_3 + \ldots$$

Note that the total resistance is greater than each individual resistance.

■ *e.g.* The *potential divider* comprises resistors in series.

resolution of a vector: see *vector resolution*.

resonance: a phenomenon that occurs when the frequency at which an object is being made to vibrate (the *forced frequency of vibration*) is equal to its *natural frequency of vibration*.

■ The amplitude of vibration is a maximum at this frequency and is limited solely by the degree of damping. The effect of increased damping is to:

- reduce the amplitude of vibration at all frequencies
- reduce the sharpness of the resonance peak
- shift the peak slightly towards lower frequencies

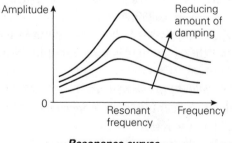

Resonance curves

▦ *e.g.* Resonance tube, tuning a radio.

▦ *TIP* When defining resonance, do not forget to include 'vibrating at maximum amplitude'. Many students discuss frequency without mentioning amplitude.

resultant: the name given to a single vector that is equivalent, in magnitude and direction, to two or more vectors.

▦ The resultant of two vectors may be found using a *vector triangle*.

▦ *TIP* If you are asked to find a resultant, this automatically implies direction as well as magnitude.

retardation: a decrease in the velocity of an object; it is defined as being a negative acceleration, where acceleration is measured in the direction of travel of the object.

▦ An alternative name for retardation is *deceleration*.

right-hand grip rule: a technique used to find the direction of the magnetic field inside a flat coil or a solenoid.

▦ If you imagine grasping the coil in your right hand, with your fingers pointing in the direction of the current, then your thumb gives the direction of the magnetic field. (See also *magnetic flux density due to a coil*.)

ripple tank: a shallow tank of water used to demonstrate wave phenomena.

▦ The tank has a transparent base and the water has a depth of about 1 cm. A vibrator sets up ripples on the surface of the water. Plane wavefronts are produced by a long straight vibrator touching the water surface, and circular wavefronts radiate from a small pointed vibrator. The wavelength of the ripples may be changed by changing the frequency of the vibrator. Generally, the tank is illuminated from above and the ripples are observed as 'shadows' on a screen below the tank.

▦ *e.g.* A ripple tank may be used to demonstrate *reflection, refraction, diffraction* and *interference* of waves.

rms speed: see *root-mean-square speed*.

root-mean-square speed (rms speed): the square root of the mean, or average, value of the molecular speed squared; its symbol is $\sqrt{<c^2>}$ or c_{rms}.

▦ If $c_1, c_2, c_3, c_4, c_5 \ldots c_N$ are the speeds at any one time of N molecules of a gas, then the root-mean-square speed is given by

$$c_{rms} = \sqrt{[(c_1^2 + c_2^2 + c_3^2 + c_4^2 + c_5^2 + \ldots c_N^2)/N]}$$

Although the rms speed is defined above, it is never calculated using this equation. The quantity calculated using equations based on the kinetic theory of gases is the mean square speed $<c^2>$. By taking the square root of this quantity, we have the rms speed, which tells us something about the speeds of the molecules. Note that the rms speed is not the same as the mean speed.

▦ *e.g.* It is used in the *kinetic theory of gases*.

Rutherford model of the atom: a model proposed in 1911 in which the atom was conceived as a very small positively charged nucleus containing most of the mass of the atom, around which orbits a number of negatively charged electrons; the number of electrons is such as to make the overall charge on the atom neutral.

The electrons were thought to orbit at very high speeds such that they could be thought of as clouds of negative charge known as orbitals. (See also *energy levels*; *emission spectrum*.)

saturated vapour: see *vapour*.

saturated vapour pressure (SVP): see *vapour*.

scalar quantity (also called just 'scalar')**:** a quantity that has magnitude only, not direction.

▓ Scalar quantities are described fully by giving their magnitude and unit. Scalars can be added algebraically.

▓ *e.g. Mass, speed, energy* are scalar quantities.

▓ *TIP* Look carefully at the situation in which the quantity is being used. 'Distance between two objects' has magnitude only and is a scalar. However, 'distance from a fixed point' may involve direction and would then be a *vector quantity*.

scales of temperature: see *temperature scale*.

scintillation counter: a counter designed to measure the count rate from a radioactive source.

▓ The scintillator produces a small flash of light whenever a particle or photon of radiation from a source is incident on it. A photomultiplier tube converts each flash of light into a pulse of current. The current pulses can then be detected and counted. Scintillation counters will provide information about the distribution of energy in the radiation, as well as identifying the type of radiation.

semiconductor: a material that is an insulator at absolute zero but a conductor at higher temperatures.

▓ As temperature rises, the number of *charge carriers* available to carry electric current increases. Semiconductor materials may be produced such that the majority of charge carriers are either negatively charged or positively charged. (See also *diode; light-emitting diode; light-dependent resistor*.)

▓ *e.g.* Semiconductor materials are at the foundation of the modern electronics industry.

shm: see *simple harmonic motion*

sign convention: see *lens formula*.

simple harmonic motion (shm): the motion of an object such that its acceleration is proportional to its displacement from a fixed point and is always directed towards that point.

■ For an object having displacement x and acceleration a, simple harmonic motion is defined by the equation

$$a = -\omega^2 x$$

The minus sign shows that the acceleration is always directed towards the fixed point where $x = 0$, and ω^2 is a constant.

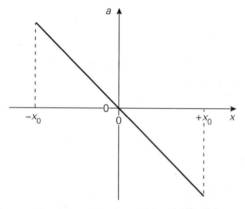

Variation with displacement x of the acceleration a for shm

The gradient of the graph is $-\omega^2$ and x_0 is the *amplitude* of the motion. The physical significance of the constant ω^2 is that its square root (ω) is related to the period T of the oscillations by the expression

$$T = 2\pi/\omega$$

Since frequency f is given by $f = 1/T$, it follows that

$$\omega = 2\pi/T = 2\pi f$$

The constant ω is referred to as the angular frequency and is measured in radians per second ($\text{rad}\,\text{s}^{-1}$).

simple harmonic motion, energy of: the kinetic energy, potential energy and total energy associated with an object undergoing simple harmonic motion.

■ If the motion is undamped, there is a continuous interchange between kinetic energy E_k and potential energy E_p, with the total energy E_t remaining constant. For an object of mass m vibrating at frequency f (angular frequency $\omega = 2\pi f$) and having amplitude x_0

potential energy $E_p = \frac{1}{2}m\omega^2 x^2 = 2m\pi^2 f^2 x^2$

kinetic energy $E_k = \frac{1}{2}m\omega^2(x_0^2 - x^2) = 2m\pi^2 f^2(x_0^2 - x^2)$

total energy $E_t = E_p + E_k = \frac{1}{2}m\omega^2 x_0^2 = 2m\pi^2 f^2 x_0^2$

The variation with time t of the energy is shown in the diagram below. Note that one solution for displacement has been included in order that phase may be illustrated.

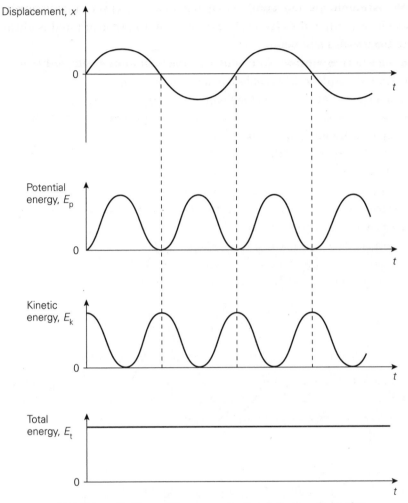

Variation with time of the energy in simple harmonic motion

The variations with displacement x of E_p, E_k and E_t are shown in the diagram below.

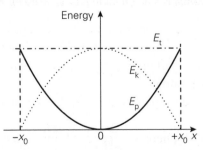

Variation with displacement of the energy in simple harmonic motion

TIP The graphs for the variation with time of E_p and E_k have twice the frequency of that for the displacement x. Furthermore, the curves are sinusoidal, not 'half-wave rectified'.

simple harmonic motion, solutions: equations describing the motion of an object that is moving with *simple harmonic motion* (shm).

For an object of mass m oscillating with amplitude x_0 and frequency f

period $T = 1/f$

angular frequency $\omega = 2\pi f$

If $x = 0$ when time $t = 0$, then

displacement $x = x_0 \sin\omega t = x_0 \sin 2\pi ft$

velocity $v = x_0\omega \cos\omega t = 2\pi fx_0 \cos 2\pi ft$

acceleration: $a = -\omega^2 x = -\omega^2 x_0 \sin\omega t = -4\pi^2 f^2 x_0 \sin 2\pi ft$

If $x = x_0$ when time $t = 0$, then

displacement $x = x_0 \cos\omega t = x_0 \cos 2\pi ft$

velocity $v = -x_0\omega \sin\omega t = -2\pi fx_0 \sin 2\pi ft$

acceleration $a = -\omega^2 x = -\omega^2 x_0 \cos\omega t = -4\pi^2 f^2 x_0 \cos 2\pi ft$

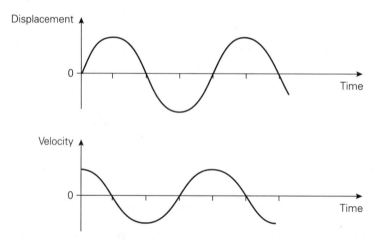

Displacement–time graph to give velocity for shm

TIP You may be asked to solve one or more of these equations to find displacement, velocity, etc. The starting point is to calculate the angular frequency ω. Also, pay attention to the start of the motion; this determines whether sine or cosine functions are appropriate.

simple pendulum: ideally, a point mass suspended on a light, inextensible flexible thread.

In practice, a small metal sphere is suspended from a fixed point by a piece of flexible thread. The metal sphere (pendulum bob) is given a small displacement and then released so that the bob oscillates in a vertical plane.

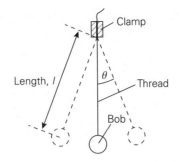

The period T of the oscillations is related to the length l of the pendulum by the expression

$T = 2\pi\sqrt{(l/g)}$

where g is the acceleration of free fall. The length l is measured from the point of support to the centre of mass of the bob. The formula is true for small oscillations only: the angle θ must be less than about 5°.

■ *e.g.* May be used for the determination of the acceleration of free fall g.

■ *TIP* If you are asked to describe a method for the determination of g by free fall, do not describe a method involving a simple pendulum. A simple pendulum is not 'free fall'.

sinusoidal: a variation with time of a quantity, in the form of either a sine wave or a cosine wave.

■ The important point here is the general shape of the wave. Whether the variation is in the form of a sine wave or a cosine wave determines the *phase*.

SI system: the internationally agreed basis for the measurement of physical quantities and for the units to define the sizes of the quantities.

■ SI is the abbreviation for Système International d'Unités. The SI system is established by reference to seven *base quantities* and their associated *base units* of measurement.

slide-wire potentiometer: see *potentiometer, slide-wire*.

smoothing: the process whereby a half-wave or a full-wave rectified voltage is made more constant in value (see *rectification*).

■ The voltage output of a rectifier is direct, but its value varies between zero and a maximum. This voltage V_{IN} is applied to a smoothing circuit.

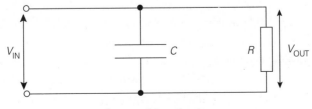

A smoothing circuit

The capacitor of capacitance C charges up when V_{IN} rises. When V_{IN} falls, the capacitor discharges through the load of resistance R. The capacitor then recharges when V_{IN} rises and the process repeats itself.

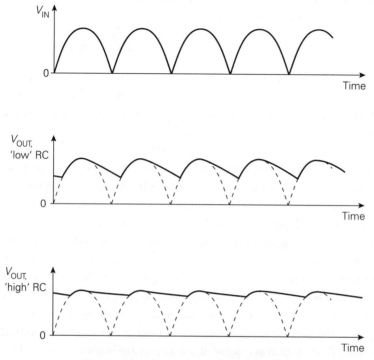

Input and output voltages for a smoothing circuit

The amount of 'ripple' on the smoothed output depends on the product RC (see *capacitor discharge*). The larger the value of RC, the longer it takes for the capacitor to discharge and therefore the smaller the 'ripple'.

soft iron: iron that can be easily magnetised and demagnetised.

▨ Soft iron increases the magnetic field strength by up to 1000 times above that which would be obtained in a vacuum.

▨ *e.g.* Soft iron is used in *electromagnets* and *transformers*.

solid: one of the four states of matter.

▨ A solid is characterised by having a fixed volume and a fixed shape. There are strong attractive forces (bonds) between the atoms and molecules of a solid, holding them in fixed positions within the solid. The molecules do vibrate about the fixed positions, the amplitude of vibration increasing with temperature rise. Hence a solid expands on heating. A solid and a *liquid* have approximately the same density, suggesting that the separation of molecules is about the same in both. The separation of molecules is about one-tenth of that in a *gas*.

sonometer: a hollow wooden box, across which may be stretched a string or wire.

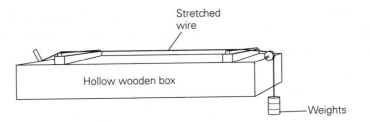

Stretched wire

Hollow wooden box

Weights

The purpose of the sonometer box is to increase the loudness of the sound produced by a vibrating string, thus enabling easier detection of the vibrations.

■ *e.g.* Used to investigate *stationary waves on strings*, and in musical instruments.

sound: a pressure wave which is detected by the ear.

■ The *frequency* or *pitch* of audible sound is generally assumed to be in the range 20 Hz to 15 kHz, although this range does vary with age, state of health etc. Sound above the audible range is referred to as *ultrasound*. The loudness of a sound depends on the amplitude of the pressure wave. Loud sounds will have a pressure amplitude of about 50 Pa but a person with good hearing can detect waves with a pressure amplitude of 10^{-5} Pa (atmospheric pressure is about 10^5 Pa).

sound waves: pressure waves which move through a medium and are caused by vibrating objects.

■ Consider a loudspeaker in air. When the loudspeaker is working, its cone moves backwards and forwards, expanding and compressing the air immediately in contact with it. When the air is expanded, a low-pressure region — a *rarefaction* — is produced and this moves outwards through the air. The cone then moves forwards, producing a high-pressure region — a *compression* — which also moves outwards from the cone. The sound wave consists of a series of compressions and rarefactions that move through the air. Particles within the medium vibrate, transferring the pressure changes through the medium. There is no transfer of the medium itself, only a transfer of wave energy. Sound waves are *longitudinal waves* that must have a medium for the transfer of wave energy. The speed of sound in a medium depends on its *density* and its *elasticity*.

specific charge: the ratio of the charge on a particle to its mass; its SI unit is coulomb per kilogram (C kg^{-1}).

■ The measurement of specific charge is one means by which particles can be identified.

■ *e.g.* Specific charge of an electron is -1.76×10^{11} C kg^{-1}; specific charge of a proton is 9.58×10^7 C kg^{-1}.

specific heat capacity: a value that is numerically equal to the amount of thermal energy required to raise the temperature of unit mass of the substance by one degree.

■ Specific heat capacity is a property of a substance and, over a limited range of temperature, its value may be assumed to be constant. The SI unit is joule per kilogram per kelvin ($J\,kg^{-1}\,K^{-1}$). For an object of mass m and specific heat capacity c, the amount of thermal energy ΔQ required to raise the temperature by $\Delta\theta$ is given by

$$\Delta Q = mc\Delta\theta$$

The same equation applies for a decrease in thermal energy and a temperature fall.

specific latent heat: a value that is numerically equal to the thermal energy transferred when unit mass of a substance changes state, without any change of temperature.

■ For a change of state from solid to liquid, or from liquid to solid, the latent heat is referred to as latent heat of fusion. When the change is from liquid to vapour (gas) or from vapour to liquid, latent heat of vaporisation is involved. Specific latent heat is a property of a substance. The SI unit is joule per kilogram ($J\,kg^{-1}$). For an object of mass m and specific latent heat L, the amount of thermal energy ΔQ transferred during a change of state is given by

$$\Delta Q = mL$$

The thermal energy involved in changes of state is referred to as 'latent', or 'hidden', because no temperature change is involved. Thermal energy is supplied to convert a solid to a liquid or to convert a liquid to a vapour (gas). The thermal energy is given out when the changes are in the opposite directions.

■ *TIP* Remember that no temperature change is involved in latent heat.

speed: a scalar quantity defined by the word equation

$$\text{speed} = \frac{\text{distance travelled}}{\text{time taken}}$$

■ The SI unit of speed is metre per second ($m\,s^{-1}$). Since distance travelled can only ever increase, speed is always a positive quantity. When equal distances are travelled in equal times, the speed is constant and is said to be uniform. When the speed varies, the average speed is calculated using the equation

$$\text{average speed} = \frac{\text{total distance travelled}}{\text{total time taken}}$$

Speed can be calculated from the gradient of a *distance–time graph*.

■ *TIP* When finding the gradient of any graph, use a large triangle so that the gradient has as small an uncertainty as possible.

speed of light: by definition, the speed of light is $299\ 792\ 458\,m\,s^{-1}$ in a vacuum.

■ All *electromagnetic waves* in a vacuum have this speed. The speed in a medium can be determined if the *refractive index* of the medium is known. Some books refer to the 'velocity of light'. This is not correct since light has the same speed in all directions.

■ *TIP* For general calculations, the value $3.00 \times 10^8\,m\,s^{-1}$ is assumed.

speed–time graph: a graph showing how speed (*y*-axis) varies with time (*x*-axis).

▨ The area between the line of the graph and the *x*-axis represents the distance moved in the particular interval of time.

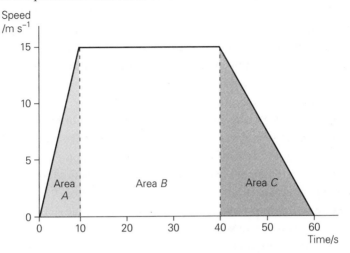

Distance travelled is represented by area *A* + area *B* + area *C*. On the speed–time graph shown this is

distance = $(\frac{1}{2} \times 15 \times 10) + (15 \times 30) + (\frac{1}{2} \times 15 \times 20) = 675$ m

When the speed–time graph is a curve, distance travelled may be estimated by 'counting squares'.

▨ ***TIP*** Since speed is a scalar quantity, it cannot have a negative value.

spiral spring: a spring formed by winding a wire in a spiral.

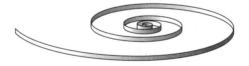

▨ In general, one end of the spring is fixed. The torque *T* required to wind the spring through angle θ is given by

$T = c\theta$

where *c* is a constant.

▨ ***e.g.*** Control springs in moving-coil meters and clock springs.

spontaneity: a term used to describe radioactive decay.

▨ Radioactive decay is said to be spontaneous because it is unaffected by environmental factors such as temperature and pressure. This does mean that *half-life* is a constant for any particular nuclide.

spring constant (also called 'elastic constant'): the constant of proportionality between force *F* and extension Δx for a sample of material that has not been stretched to such an extent that it has exceeded the *elastic limit*.

$$F = k\Delta x$$

where k is the spring constant (elastic constant). Spring constant is the force per unit extension and is measured in newton per metre ($N\,m^{-1}$).

■ *e.g.* The spring constant is relevant to the extension of springs and wires. (See also *Hooke's law*.)

■ *TIP* Although named 'spring constant', the constant applies not only to springs but also to the extension of an object of any shape where the elastic limit has not been exceeded.

stability: the state of a body that is in *equilibrium*.

■ A body may be in *stable equilibrium*, *unstable equilibrium* or *neutral equilibrium*.

stable equilibrium: a body is in stable *equilibrium* if it will return to its original position after it has been displaced slightly.

■ *e.g.* A small ball in a spherical bowl — when the ball is displaced, it will come to rest in its original position in the bottom of the bowl.

standard atmospheric pressure: defined as being $1.01325 \times 10^5\,Pa$.

■ *e.g.* Reference is made to standard atmospheric pressure when defining the *ice point* and the *steam point*.

standing wave: see *stationary wave*.

stationary wave (also called 'standing wave')**:** a wave in which vibrational energy is stored, rather than transmitted as in a *progressive wave*.

■ A stationary wave is the result of two progressive waves, of the same frequency, travelling in opposite directions along the same line. If the phase difference between the two waves is correct, a stationary wave is formed.

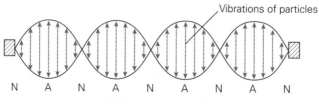

Vibrations of particles

N   A   N   A   N   A   N   A   N

A stationary wave on a string

The diagram illustrates a stationary wave on a string. When the string was plucked, waves travelled outwards from the point of plucking in both directions. The waves were reflected at the ends of the string, causing the waves to overlap. The resultant wave appears not to move. At certain points, the two waves meet in *antiphase*, resulting in complete *destructive interference* — a *node* N. Where the waves meet in phase, the amplitude is a maximum — an *antinode* A is formed. Between any two nodes, all the particles vibrate in phase but have different amplitudes. There is a phase difference of $\pi\,rad$ between the vibrations of a particle in one nodal loop and those of a particle in a neighbouring loop.

The distance between two adjacent nodes (or antinodes) is one half wavelength of the stationary wave. (See also *stationary wave in a pipe*; *resonance*.)

■ **TIP** Remember that the internodal distance is one half wavelength, not one wavelength. Always draw stationary waves showing the two extremes of amplitude; if only one extreme is drawn, the diagram will look like the representation of a progressive wave.

stationary wave in a pipe: a particular form of *stationary wave* that is created by blowing across the end of a pipe.

■ A wave is started at one end of the pipe by blowing air across it. The wave travels down the pipe and is reflected at the other end, thus producing two waves travelling in opposite directions which may interfere to produce a stationary wave.

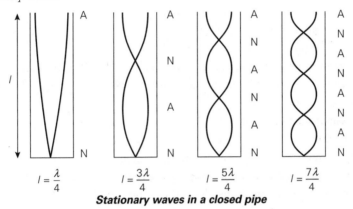

Stationary waves in a closed pipe

A closed pipe is closed at one end only. A *node* must be formed at the closed end where the air cannot move and an *antinode* is formed at the open end. The wavelength of the stationary wave in the pipe is λ. Note that the stationary wave is represented by drawing displacements of the particles at right angles to the axis of the pipe although the displacements are, in fact, along its axis. Stationary waves are also formed in pipes open at both ends (open pipes).

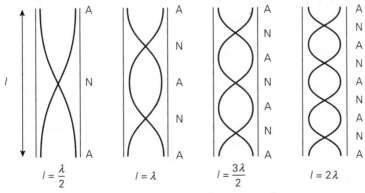

Stationary waves in an open pipe

As the pipe is open at both ends, an antinode exists at both ends. The distance between two neighbouring nodes or two neighbouring antinodes is one half wavelength of the wave. In practice, the antinode at the open end of a pipe occurs just outside the pipe.

■ *e.g.* Stationary waves in pipes are the source of sound in many musical instruments, including woodwind, brass and organ.

stationary wave on a string: a particular form of *stationary wave* produced by plucking or bowing a stretched string.

■ Two progressive waves, moving in opposite directions along the string, interfere to produce a stationary wave.

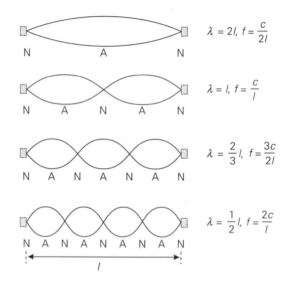

$$\lambda = 2l, \ f = \frac{c}{2l}$$

$$\lambda = l, \ f = \frac{c}{l}$$

$$\lambda = \frac{2}{3}l, \ f = \frac{3c}{2l}$$

$$\lambda = \frac{1}{2}l, \ f = \frac{2c}{l}$$

In the diagram, l is the length of the string, λ, f and c are the wavelength, frequency and speed of the waves, respectively. For a stationary wave to be set up, there must be a *node* at each end of the string. The frequency of vibration of the string determines the number of internodal loops that fit exactly into the length of the string. The speed c of the waves on the string is given by

$$c = \surd(T/m)$$

where T is the tension in the string and m is the mass per unit length of the string.

■ *e.g.* Stationary waves in strings are the source of the sound produced by stringed musical instruments. They can be investigated using a *sonometer*.

steam point: the temperature of steam in thermal equilibrium with pure water at standard atmospheric pressure.

■ By definition, this temperature is one hundred degrees Centigrade (100°C). It is 373.15 K.

Stokes' law: a law that provides an expression for the viscous (drag) force F

opposing the streamline flow of a sphere of radius *r* through a fluid with *coefficient of viscosity η*:

$$F = 6\pi r \eta v$$

where *v* is the speed of the sphere relative to the fluid.

▨ *e.g.* The formula is used in the theory of *Millikan's oil drop experiment*.

straight-line graph, equation of: an equation representing a straight-line graph of gradient *m* and *y-intercept c*:

$$y = mx + c$$

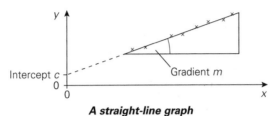

A straight-line graph

▨ In experimental physics, a straight-line graph is frequently drawn in order to find the relationship between two variables. For example, suppose that a quantity *P* varies with quantity *Q* according to the expression

$$P = aQ^n$$

and the task is to find the constants *a* and *n*. Taking logarithms of the equation gives

$$\lg P = \lg a + n\lg Q$$

Rearranging the equation as

$$\lg P = n\lg Q + \lg a$$

and then comparing this with *y* = *mx* + *c*, it can be seen that *n* is the gradient of the graph and lg*a* is the intercept on the *y*-axis.

strain (also, more correctly, called 'tensile strain'): the change in length per unit length of a sample of material; it is usually given the symbol *ε*.

▨ Tensile strain is the ratio of two lengths and therefore has no unit. There are other forms of strain, due to twisting or to volume changes. However, in AS/A-level physics we are usually only concerned with tensile strain (changes in length). Consequently, we often merely refer to 'strain', assuming that it is tensile strain.

▨ *e.g.* Tensile strain is one of the terms used to define the *Young modulus*.

▨ *TIP* Remember that (tensile) strain is a property of the material that does not depend on the length of the sample. It is, however, dependent on the applied stress.

strain energy: the energy stored in a sample of material as a result of a stress being applied to the sample; its SI unit is the joule (J).

▨ If a graph of load *F* is plotted against extension Δ*x*, the area between the graph line and the *x*-axis gives a measure of strain energy.

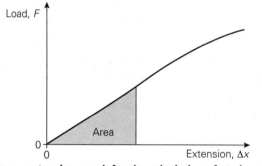

Force–extension graph for the calculation of strain energy

For an elastic change, since the graph is a straight line

$$\text{strain energy} = \tfrac{1}{2} F\Delta x$$

But the spring constant $k = F/\Delta x$. Hence

$$\text{strain energy} = \tfrac{1}{2} k(\Delta x)^2$$

Strain energy is recovered if the change in the sample is elastic. For plastic changes, some of this energy is used to alter the structure of the material.

strain gauge: an electrical circuit component used to measure the *strain* in a material.

▓ The gauge consists of a thin metal foil encapsulated in a thin plastic material.

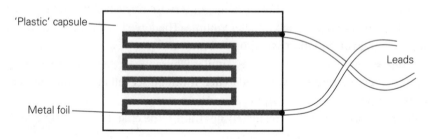

The gauge is firmly attached to the object to be strained. As the object is strained, the length and cross-sectional area of the strain gauge are changed, thus altering its resistance. The fractional change in resistance of the gauge is proportional to the strain.

▓ *e.g.* The gauge is frequently placed in a type of *potentiometer* circuit in order to measure the resistance change.

streamline flow (also called 'laminar flow'): the smooth steady flow of a fluid without any disturbances such as eddies.

▓ Streamlines show the path of the moving fluid and, at any point, the direction of flow of the fluid is the tangent to the streamline. In general, streamline flow only occurs when the fluid speed is low. At higher speeds, *turbulent flow* occurs. *Stokes' law* and *Poiseuille's equation* apply to streamline flow.

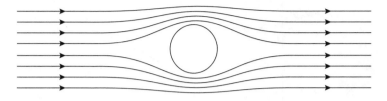

streamlines: see *streamline flow.*

strength: see *breaking stress.*

stress (also, more correctly, called 'tensile stress')**:** the tensile force per unit area applied to a sample of material; it is usually given the symbol σ.

■ The force is normal to the area. The SI unit of stress is newton per metre squared ($N\,m^{-2}$) or *pascal* (Pa). There are other forms of stress: shear stress, which produces twisting, and volume stress, which produces changes in volume. However, these are not usually studied in AS/A-level physics. Consequently, we often merely refer to 'stress', assuming that it is tensile stress.

■ *e.g.* Tensile stress is one of the terms used to define the *Young modulus.*

strong nuclear force: the force within the nucleus that binds the *nucleons* together.

■ This force must be attractive at short range (i.e. distances of the order of the radius of a nucleus) to bind together protons in the nucleus. However, it must become repulsive at even shorter range, otherwise nucleons would be pulled together into an increasingly smaller volume. The force is transmitted through the exchange of mesons. (See also *weak nuclear force.*)

superposition: the combining of two similar waves when they meet at a point.

■ The *principle of superposition* is used to determine the resultant displacement at the point.

systematic errors: see *uncertainty.*

temperature: a *base quantity* in the *SI system*; its unit is the kelvin (K).

■ It is a measure of the degree of hotness of an object. Thermal energy moves of its own accord from objects at a higher temperature to objects at a lower temperature. (See also *temperature scale*.)

■ *TIP* It is important to realise that temperature does not measure the amount of thermal energy in an object (see *specific latent heat*). It does indicate in which direction thermal energy will flow unaided.

temperature scale: a numerical scale on which the degree of hotness of a body is expressed.

■ Originally, temperature scales were established in an arbitrary way and involved a property of a substance that changes with temperature (*empirical scales of temperature*). It is now realised that temperature is not an arbitrary quantity and is defined within thermodynamics (the *thermodynamic scale of temperature*).

tensile forces: two forces acting in opposite directions on an object so as to tend to increase its length along the direction of the forces.

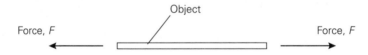

Object

Force, *F*   Force, *F*

■ The forces do not cause any translational or rotational motion of the object. (See also *Young modulus*.)

■ *e.g.* The forces that cause the extension of a spring.

■ *TIP* Remember that two forces are involved, although we may only show one of them on a diagram. An example is a spring suspended from a fixed point, supporting a load. The load is, obviously, one of the two forces. The other force is supplied by the support.

tera-: prefix used with a unit to denote the multiple of $\times 10^{12}$; its symbol is T.

■ *e.g.* 1 terametre $= 1 \times 10^{12}\,\mathrm{m} = 1\,\mathrm{Tm}$

terminal velocity: the constant velocity achieved by an object when it is falling under gravity through a viscous fluid.

In general, three forces act on the object: its weight W acting downwards, the upthrust U equal to the weight of fluid displaced acting upwards and the drag force D also acting upwards:

Accelerating force $F = W - D - U$

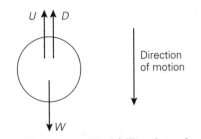

Forces acting on an object falling through a fluid

As the speed of the object increases, the drag force D increases and thus the accelerating force F decreases. Eventually, as the speed increases, the accelerating force will become zero and the object will fall at constant velocity — the terminal velocity. Terminal velocity depends on the shape and mass of the object and on the viscosity of the fluid.

TIP Remember that, as the accelerating force is decreasing, the velocity is still increasing, but the rate of increase is becoming smaller. A common mistake is to think that, as the accelerating force decreases, the velocity decreases.

tesla, T: the SI unit of magnetic flux density, that is, the 'strength' of a magnetic field.

The tesla is defined by reference to the equation for the *motor effect*, namely

$F = BIL \sin\theta$

If a conductor carrying a current of 1 amp is placed at right angles to a uniform magnetic field of flux density 1 tesla, then the force per unit length on the conductor is 1 newton per metre. The tesla is sometimes referred to as weber per metre squared ($Wb\,m^{-2}$): $1\,T = 1\,Wb\,m^{-2}$. The base units of the tesla are $kg\,s^{-2}\,A^{-1}$.

thermal capacity (also called 'heat capacity'): a value numerically equal to the quantity of heat required to raise the temperature of the whole object by one degree.

In the SI system, thermal capacity is measured in joule per kelvin ($J\,K^{-1}$). For an object of thermal capacity C having a temperature change $\Delta\theta$, the change in thermal (heat) energy ΔQ is given by

$\Delta Q = C\Delta\theta$

Thermal (heat) capacity is frequently used when an object is made up of a number of different materials so that there is no single value of *specific heat capacity*. The mass of the object is not required. For a single substance of mass m and specific heat capacity c, the thermal capacity C of the substance is given by

$C = mc$

thermal fission reactor: a power plant using the energy released when heavy elements such as uranium-235 are fissioned by means of neutrons.

■ The nuclear reaction may be summarised as follows:

$$^{235}_{92}U + ^1_0n \longrightarrow X + Y + (2 \text{ or } 3 \text{ neutrons}) + \gamma\text{-ray photons} + \text{energy}$$

where X and Y are nuclei having approximately equal masses.

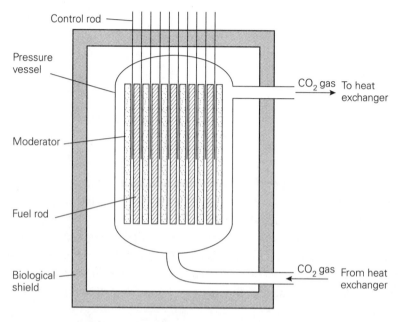

A schematic diagram of one type of nuclear reactor

The uranium is contained in hollow fuel rods, surrounded by a graphite moderator. The moderator slows down the fast-moving neutrons so that they may continue the *chain reaction*. The chain reaction is controlled by means of control rods made of boron steel. These absorb neutrons and thus determine how many neutrons are available to continue the chain reaction. Inserting the control rods into the reactor core slows down the rate of reaction. Much of the energy of the fission reaction is seen as kinetic energy of the fission fragments X and Y. When these fragments are slowed down, the reactor heats up. This thermal energy is removed by means of a coolant (e.g. high-pressure carbon dioxide). Pumping the gas through a heat exchanger allows the production of high-pressure steam that can be used to drive turbines for the generation of electric power in dynamos. The reactor is sited in a pressure vessel to ensure containment of the highly radioactive fission fragments and also to act as a biological shield against radiation.

thermionic effect (also called 'thermionic emission'): the giving-off of electrons from the surface of a hot metal.

■ In general, the metal has to be heated to at least dull-red so that the electrons gain sufficient energy to escape from its surface. Emission of electrons causes positive charge to build up on the metal. For thermionic emission to continue, the metal must be part of an electrical circuit.

■ **e.g.** A heated metal filament provides the electrons for the operation of oscilloscopes, televisions and X-ray tubes. The filament acts as the cathode in the tube.

thermionic emission: see *thermionic effect.*

thermistor: a resistor whose *resistance* varies greatly with temperature.

■ A negative temperature coefficient (ntc) thermistor shows a rapid decrease in resistance as its temperature rises. Conversely, a positive temperature coefficient (ptc) thermistor shows a rapid rise in resistance as its temperature rises. Typically, for an ntc thermistor

　　resistance at 0°C ≈ 4000 Ω
　　resistance at 30°C ≈ 1200 Ω

The variation of resistance with temperature is not linear but is frequently *exponential*, varying as $e^{b/T}$ where b is a constant and T is the thermodynamic temperature.

■ **e.g.** Thermistors are used in *potential divider* circuits for the monitoring and control of temperatures.

thermistor thermometer: thermometer using the change in resistance with temperature change of a *thermistor.*

■ Thermistor thermometers are available to cover the temperature range from about −50°C to +300°C. They are not direct reading but do have the advantage that they are remote reading and, since the output is electrical, the output data can be stored easily. (See also *liquid-in-glass thermometer; thermocouple thermometer.*)

thermocouple thermometer: thermometer based on the principle of the thermocouple.

■ When the junctions of two dissimilar metals are at different temperatures, an *electromotive force* (emf) is generated between the junctions.

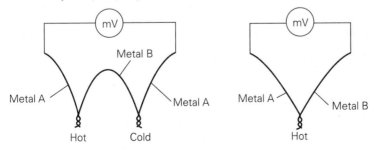

Thermocouple arrangements

The cold junction may, in fact, be the instrument used for measuring the emf. The magnitude of the emf is dependent on the temperature difference between the junctions. Thermocouple thermometers can be designed so that a very wide range of measurement of temperature (up to about 1700°C) is possible. Such thermometers are robust and have a small thermal capacity. They are remote reading and their output data can be stored easily. (See also *liquid-in-glass thermometer*; *thermistor thermometer*.)

thermodynamic scale of temperature (also called 'absolute scale of temperature' and 'Kelvin scale of temperature'): a temperature scale based on the theoretical efficiency of a perfectly reversible heat engine.

■ It is a theoretical scale that is important because it does not depend on the way that a physical property of a substance changes with temperature. The theory of perfectly reversible heat engines is not dealt with at AS/A-level, but it is important to realise that there does exist an absolute scale of temperature. The symbol for thermodynamic temperature (Kelvin temperature) is T and, since the scale was developed by Lord Kelvin, the unit is the kelvin (symbol K). The temperature at which any object has minimum energy is zero kelvin (0 K). The kelvin is the fraction 1/273.16 of the difference between the absolute zero of temperature and the *triple point* of water. Since the temperature of the triple point of water is 0.01 K above the freezing point of water at standard atmospheric pressure, the Celsius temperature t is related to Kelvin temperature T by the expression

$$t/°C = T/K - 273.15$$

■ *TIP* Note that reference to the triple point of water in the definition of the kelvin attaches a numerical value to the thermodynamic scale of temperature. A single reference temperature (apart from the zero of the scale) is used and the scale does not rely on a change in a property of a real substance with temperature. For many calculations at AS/A-level where two or three significant figure accuracy is required, the conversion $t/°C = T/K - 273$ is satisfactory. However, you must be aware of the full conversion.

threshold frequency: the minimum frequency of electromagnetic radiation incident on a surface for the *photoelectric effect* to take place.

■ The threshold frequency depends on the nature of the material and on its surface condition. The *work function energy* ϕ is related to the threshold frequency f_0 by the expression

$$\phi = hf_0$$

where h is the *Planck constant*.

time: a *base quantity* in the *SI system*; its unit is the second (s).

■ One second is the time taken for 9 192 631 770 periods of the radiation emitted during a transition between two *energy levels* in the ground state of a caesium-133 atom.

time constant: the time taken for the potential difference across a capacitor, discharging through a resistor, to fall to a fraction 1/e of an earlier value.

■ Time constant may also be defined in terms of the charge on the capacitor or the current in the resistor. The form of the *capacitor discharge* is exponential and the time needed for the fractional change 1/e does not depend on the initial value. Time constant is given the symbol τ and has the unit of time (s). Since, for capacitor discharge, the potential difference V varies with time t according to

$$V = V_0\,e^{-t/RC}$$

and, by definition, when $t = \tau$ then $V/V_0 = 1/e = e^{-1}$, it follows that

$$\tau/RC = 1$$

and

time constant $\tau = RC$

Note that time constant also applies to the charging of a capacitor through a resistor.

■ *e.g.* Time constant is important when determining the amount of *smoothing* of a direct voltage or current.

■ *TIP* The equation $\tau = RC$ is an important equation and must be learned. However, it should not be used as the definition of time constant.

torque: the torque of a *couple* is the turning effect of the couple.

■ For two equal but opposite parallel forces, each of magnitude F, with their lines of action separated by a distance d, the magnitude of the turning effect of the couple (the torque of the couple) is given by

torque of couple $= Fd$

Torque is a *vector quantity* and its SI unit is newton metre (N m).

■ *TIP* Do not confuse the unit of torque with that of energy (the joule). Both are the product of a force and a distance, but in the case of torque the force and distance are at right angles, while for energy the force and distance moved are along the same line.

total internal reflection: total reflection of a wave incident on a boundary between two media.

■ It occurs when the wave is incident from the more dense medium and the angle of incidence of the wave is greater than its *critical angle*.

■ *e.g.* It is the basis of our understanding of *reflecting prisms* and *optic fibres*.

toughness: a measure of the amount of work which must be done, or of the amount of energy stored in a material, before it breaks.

■ *TIP* Toughness should not be confused with strength. Glass is a strong material, i.e. it has a high breaking stress, but it is not tough because it does not absorb much energy before failure. (See also *brittleness*.)

trajectory motion: the motion of an object which has both horizontal and vertical motion.

t

The resultant velocity or position of the object may be found by treating the horizontal motion and the vertical motion independently using the *equations of motion*. Generally, the object has a uniform velocity in one direction (horizontally) and accelerated motion in the vertical direction. Assuming that air resistance is negligible, the maximum horizontal range is obtained when the object is projected at an angle of 45° to the horizontal.

TIP When solving problems involving trajectory motion, it is usual to separate the vertically upward motion from the downward motion, remembering that the object takes as long to fall as it does to rise.

transformer: a device by which the voltage of an alternating supply may be changed.

It consists of two coils of insulated wire, a primary and a secondary, wound on a *soft iron* core.

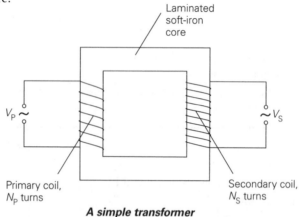

A simple transformer

An alternating voltage V_P is applied to the primary coil of N_P turns. A changing magnetic field in the core causes an *induced emf* V_S in the secondary coil of N_S turns. The core is laminated to reduce energy losses due to currents being induced in the core. If the transformer is ideal (i.e. there are no magnetic flux losses and no energy is lost in the core or the coils), then

$$V_S/V_P = N_S/N_P$$

Also, since an ideal transformer is 100% efficient

power in primary coil = power in secondary coil

If the currents in the secondary and in the primary coils are I_S and I_P, respectively

$$V_S I_S = V_P I_P$$

and

$$V_S/V_P = N_S/N_P = I_P/I_S$$

The frequency remains unchanged.

e.g. A transformer may be used in conjunction with a *rectifier*.

TIP A transformer operates only on an alternating supply.

transverse wave: a wave in which the displacements of the particles in the wave are at right angles to the direction of transfer of the energy of the wave.

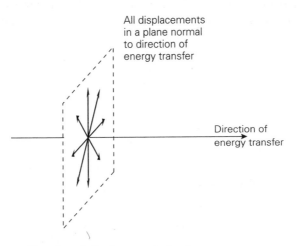

All displacements in a plane normal to direction of energy transfer

Direction of energy transfer

Direction of displacements in a transverse wave

■ *e.g.* Surface water waves and light waves (in this case there are no vibrating particles but, instead, oscillating electric and magnetic fields).

■ *TIP* When stating what is meant by a transverse wave, be very careful to specify 'direction of transfer of energy of the wave', not merely 'direction of the wave'.

triple point: the single temperature at which the solid, liquid and vapour states of a substance exist together.

■ For water, the pressure at the triple point is 610.5 Pa and the temperature is 0.01 K above the freezing point of water at standard atmospheric pressure. That is, at 273.16 K. The triple point of water is used when defining what is meant by the magnitude of the kelvin. (See also *thermodynamic scale of temperature*.)

turbulent flow: the type of flow that occurs when the speed of a fluid is sufficiently high for *streamline flow* not to occur; it is characterised by irregular paths and eddies.

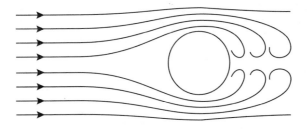

■ Drag forces in turbulent flow are greater than in streamline flow because kinetic energy must be provided to the fluid to create the eddies.

two-source interference: the pattern produced when waves from two sources meet.

▪ Suitable apparatus to demonstrate two-source interference using light is shown in the diagram below.

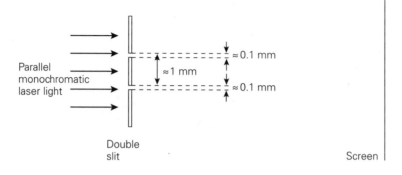

Two-source interference of light

The slits ensure that the monochromatic light emerging from them is coherent. As a result of *diffraction* of light at the slits, the waves from the two slits overlap and a series of light and dark bands is observed on the screen. Along the axis of symmetry of the apparatus, the waves from the two slits have zero *path difference* and thus *constructive interference occurs*, giving rise to a bright fringe. On either side of this line of symmetry, there will be a path difference between the waves when they meet on the screen. If this path difference is an integer number of wavelengths, constructive interference occurs and a bright fringe will be seen. For a path difference equal to an odd number of half wavelengths, *destructive interference* occurs and a dark fringe will result.

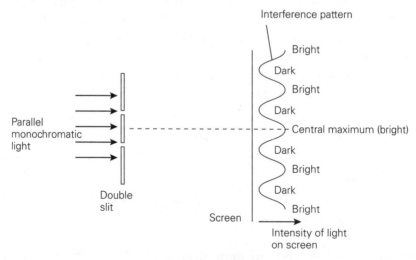

Interference fringes

If the distance D between the double slit and the screen is very much larger than the wavelength λ of the light, the fringes will be equally spaced. For a slit separation s, the fringe spacing w of the fringes is given by

$w = \lambda D/s$

Two-source interference provides a convenient means by which the wavelength of light may be found. For a typical experiment for light of wavelength 630 nm, s is about 1 mm and D about 3 m, giving fringes of width about 2 mm. Note that the fringe width is the distance between corresponding points on neighbouring bright fringes or neighbouring dark fringes. Two-source interference may also be demonstrated using two microwave sources or two loudspeakers. In each case, the two sources are connected to the same appropriate supply. A microwave detector or, in the case of sound, the ear or a microphone, may be used to detect the interference pattern.

■ *e.g.* Two-source interference may be demonstrated using a *ripple tank* or with *microwaves, sound* or *light*.

■ *TIP* For microwaves and sound the formula $w = \lambda D/s$ is usually not appropriate because the distance between the sources and the detector is not very much greater than the wavelength. Always note carefully the dimensions of the apparatus used. The diagram can never be drawn to scale, which leads many students to think that the double slit dimensions are many times their actual values.

ultimate tensile stress (also called 'breaking stress'): the maximum *stress* that can be applied to a sample of material before it breaks.

■ For many materials, 'necking' of the sample occurs once the ultimate tensile stress has been reached. The sample develops an excessively large decrease in cross-sectional area at the 'neck', resulting in a fracture in this region.

ultrasound: similar to *sound* in that it consists of pressure waves that move through a medium.

■ The frequency range of these waves is above the audible range (i.e. above about 20 kHz).

■ *e.g.* Ultrasound has many uses, including medical diagnosis. The frequencies used are of the order of MHz. Ultrasound poses less of a health risk than X-ray diagnosis.

ultraviolet radiation (UV): *electromagnetic waves* with wavelengths in the range of about 400 nm to 1 nm, lying between *visible light* and *X-rays* in the *electromagnetic spectrum*.

■ Ultraviolet light is caused by the de-excitation of electrons in higher energy levels and is produced in mercury lamps and in the sun. UV radiation has sufficient energy to break atomic bonds and can cause skin cancers and damage to eyes. Most of the UV radiation from the sun is absorbed by ozone in the upper atmosphere. UV is detected principally by its effects on photographic plates and *fluorescence*.

■ *e.g.* UV radiation will kill bacteria and can therefore be used to sterilise equipment.

uncertainty: the range of values on both sides of a measurement in which the actual value of the measurement is expected to lie.

■ A measurement quoted as 36.4 ± 0.3 cm implies that the most likely value is 36.4 cm with an uncertainty of ± 0.3 cm. That is, the actual value is likely to lie between 36.1 cm and 36.7 cm. The uncertainty in a measurement is sometimes referred to as the *error*. However, it is more correct to refer to an uncertainty where there is doubt in the reading. When a number of individuals all take the same measurement, there will be a spread of values about a mean. The uncertainty is referred to as being random and is sometimes called a *random error*. Random errors or uncertainties are seen as a scatter of readings about a mean and can be reduced by averaging. If an instrument has a *zero error*, all measurements will be too high (or too low) by a certain amount. This error is called a *systematic error*. Systematic errors cannot be eliminated by averaging but can be reduced by correct laboratory practice. (See also *accuracy; precision*.)

undamped oscillations: oscillations in which the amplitude and the total energy remain constant with time.

■ In practice, such oscillations do not occur because energy is always lost as a result of air resistance and dissipative forces within the oscillating object. However, in some cases (such as a simple pendulum), the amplitude decreases slowly with time and there is a good approximation to undamped oscillations. (See also *simple harmonic motion, energy of.*)

unified atomic mass constant: a unit of mass equal to one-twelfth of the mass of a carbon-12 (^{12}C) atom.

■ The symbol for the unified atomic mass constant is u, where

$$1\,u = 1.660\,540 \times 10^{-27}\,\text{kg}$$

The energy equivalence ($\Delta E = c^2 \Delta m$) of $1\,u$ is $1.492\,419 \times 10^{-10}\,\text{J}$ or $931.494\,\text{MeV}$.

Note that, in some literature, the symbol u, rather than u, is used to denote the unified atomic mass unit. (See also *binding energy, nuclear; mass defect.*)

■ **TIP** In order to avoid the use of 'powers of ten', the masses of nuclei are often expressed in terms of u. However, when calculating energy equivalence, do not forget to convert mass in u to mass in kg.

unified atomic mass unit: a unit of mass, the size of which is equal to one-twelfth of the mass of a carbon-12 (^{12}C) atom.

■ The symbol for the unified atomic mass constant is u, and the magnitude of the atomic mass unit u is equal to the unified atomic mass constant u, where

$$1\,u = 1.660\,540 \times 10^{-27}\,\text{kg}$$

universal constant of gravitation (also called 'gravitational constant'): the constant in the equation representing Newton's law of gravitation; its symbol is G.

■ It relates the mutual force F between two point masses M and m and their separation r

$$F = GMm/r^2$$

The constant G has the value $6.67 \times 10^{-11}\,\text{N}\,\text{m}^2\,\text{kg}^{-2}$.

universal gas law equation: see *ideal gas law.*

universe, age of: the age of the universe can be calculated using *Hubble's law.*

■ The Hubble constant, H_0, has the unit $\text{km s}^{-1}\,\text{Mpc}^{-1}$. Since the kilometre and the megaparsec are both units of distance, the unit of the Hubble constant can be expressed as s^{-1}. The reciprocal of the Hubble constant therefore represents time. This time is the time taken for the galaxies to separate to their present positions and thus represents the age of the universe.

$1/H_0 \approx 15\text{–}18$ billion years

unstable equilibrium: an object is in unstable *equilibrium* when it will not return to its original position after it has been displaced slightly and its centre of gravity falls.

■ **e.g.** A small ball on an upturned spherical bowl. When the ball is displaced, it will roll off the bowl.

■ **TIP** The difference between unstable and neutral equilibrium is that the centre of gravity falls for unstable equilibrium whereas it stays at the same height when the equilibrium is neutral.

upthrust: a force acting on an object in the vertically upward direction as a result of the object being partially or totally immersed in a fluid.

■ The magnitude of the upthrust is given by *Archimedes' principle* and is equal to the weight of fluid displaced.

UV: see *ultraviolet radiation*.

vapour: one of the four states of matter.

■ It is characterised by the molecules of matter being free to move throughout the whole vessel in which the vapour is contained. Forces between molecules are negligible and the molecules move randomly. The molecules exert a pressure on the walls of the vessel due to collisions with the walls. The pressure exerted is referred to as the vapour pressure. The maximum pressure that the vapour can exert before it condenses is known as the *saturated vapour pressure* (SVP). The SVP increases as the temperature rises. There is little to distinguish a *gas* from a vapour. It is frequently said that a vapour may be condensed by merely increasing the pressure. A gas must be cooled before pressure is applied in order to liquefy it.

vector addition: see *vector triangle*.

vector quantity (also called just 'vector'): a quantity having both magnitude and direction.

■ Vector quantities cannot be described fully unless their direction is stated. Vectors are often represented by an arrow where the length of the arrow is drawn to scale to represent the magnitude of the vector. A vector may be resolved into two components at right-angles to one another. Two vectors may be added using a *vector triangle*.

■ *e.g. Weight* is a vector — we tend not to state its direction because we just assume that it acts downwards!

vector resolution: finding the two mutually perpendicular component vectors which, when combined, would be equivalent to the single vector being examined.

■ The technique is frequently used to resolve a single force *F* into two components, one horizontal F_H and one vertical F_V. The advantage of this technique is that calculations are simplified, as any effects occurring in the direction of one component are not influenced by effects in the other perpendicular direction.

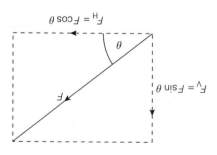

Resolution of a vector into two vertical and horizontal component vectors

■ **e.g.** Used in dynamics to separate horizontal motion from vertical motion.

■ **TIP** If a vector V is at an angle α to the direction of one component, the component along that direction is $V\cos\alpha$. The other component at right-angles to it is $V\sin\alpha$.

vector triangle: a means by which two vectors may be added to find their combined effect or *resultant*.

■ If the two vectors P and Q are represented in magnitude and direction by two sides of a triangle, then the third side represents the resultant R.

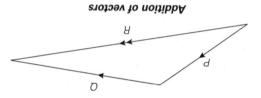

Addition of vectors

Note that the two vectors P and Q are placed in the triangle in the same direction (either both clockwise or both anticlockwise). The resultant is in the opposite direction to P and Q.

■ **TIP** When drawing a vector triangle, always indicate the scale being used. The resultant may be found by calculation to avoid drawing a scale diagram. However, it is always advisable to draw a sketch of the vector triangle.

velocity: a *vector quantity* defined by the word equation

$$\text{velocity} = \frac{\text{change of displacement}}{\text{time taken}}$$

■ The SI unit of velocity is metre per second (m s^{-1}) in a specified direction. Velocity is sometimes thought of as being 'speed in a specified direction'. A uniform velocity is a constant velocity. Average velocity may be defined as

$$\text{average velocity} = \frac{\text{total change of displacement}}{\text{total time taken}}$$

The magnitude of a velocity may be calculated as the gradient of a *displacement–time graph*.

■ **TIP** It is possible to have a constant speed but a changing velocity — an object travelling round a circle at constant speed has a continuously changing direction and thus a changing velocity.

virtual image: an image that cannot be projected on to a screen.

■ The rays of light forming this image appear to go to, or to come from, the image. The image is, in fact, formed in the mind.

■ **e.g.** An *image in a plane mirror* is a virtual image.

viscosity: the frictional forces acting between neighbouring layers of fluid when they are moving over each other at different speeds.

■ The term viscosity is now frequently used as a shortened version of *coefficient of viscosity*. Viscosity is affected by temperature: honey, for example, has a higher viscosity when cold than when hot. Gases are also viscous, but their viscosity increases with temperature rise. (See also *coefficient of viscosity*; *Stokes' law*; *Poiseuille's equation*.)

viscous forces (also called 'drag' forces): the frictional forces experienced either by an object as it moves through a fluid or by a fluid as it moves over a surface.

■ When a liquid is stirred, it is viscous forces that bring the liquid to rest again. (See also *viscosity*; *Stokes' law*; *Poiseuille's equation*.)

visible light: see *light*.

volt, V: the unit of *potential difference* (pd) and of *electromotive force* (emf); it is defined as joule per coulomb:

$$1\,V = 1\,J\,C^{-1}$$

■ The base unit of the volt is $kg\,m^2\,A^{-1}\,s^{-3}$. Alternatively, since potential difference = power/current, the volt may be defined as the watt per amp.

$$1\,V = 1\,J\,C^{-1} = 1\,W\,A^{-1}$$

■ **TIP** Although the joule per coulomb is the fundamental definition of the volt, the watt per amp is the practical definition.

voltmeter: an instrument used to measure electric potential.

■ Voltmeters may be digital or analogue. The voltmeter is connected in parallel with the component across which the potential difference is to be measured, as shown in the diagram. Note the circuit symbol for a voltmeter.

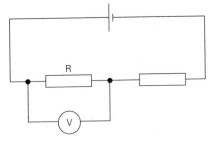

Voltmeter connected to measure the potential difference across R

watt, W: the SI unit of power; it is defined as the rate of transfer of energy of one joule per second.

$$1\,\text{W} = 1\,\text{J}\,\text{s}^{-1}$$

■ The base unit equivalent to the watt is $\text{kg}\,\text{m}^2\,\text{s}^{-3}$.

■ *TIP* It is useful, and indeed necessary, for you to be able to make reasonable estimates of quantities. A person can work at a steady rate of about 100 W whereas a high-speed electric train has motors rated in MW.

wave: a means by which energy may be transferred from one place to another as a result of oscillations.

■ *e.g.* Transverse waves, longitudinal waves and progressive waves.

wavefront: an imaginary surface that moves with a wave.

■ The surface marks out all those points on a wave that have the same *phase*. Wavefronts are usually drawn so that they are one wavelength apart and are often thought to represent wave crests.

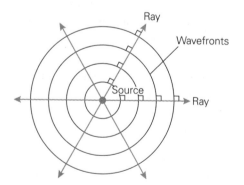

Wavefronts and rays

For wavefronts separated by one wavelength, the phase change between one wavefront and the next is 2π radians.

■ *TIP* Wavefronts are drawn at right angles to rays, which represent the direction of travel of the wave energy.

wavelength: the shortest distance between two points on a *progressive wave* which are vibrating in phase, or the distance travelled by the wave energy during one complete oscillation of the source.

■ Wavelength λ may be determined from a graph of displacement plotted against distance along the wave. The SI unit of wavelength is the metre (m).

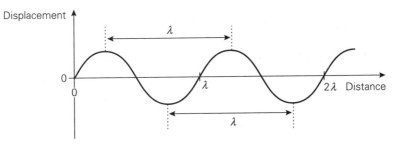

Wavelength of a wave

wave–particle duality: photons and atomic and sub-atomic particles must be treated as either particles or waves, according to circumstances.

■ Electromagnetic radiation is studied for its wave properties (diffraction and interference) but the photoelectric effect can be explained only by considering its particle nature (photons). Electrons are often considered as particles but they may be diffracted. The relation between the momentum of a particle and its associated wavelength is given by the *de Broglie equation*.

wave speed: defined in the same way as *speed*, i.e. distance travelled per unit time.

■ In this case, distance travelled is measured in the direction of the wave and is the distance travelled by the wave energy. The speed of a wave is the speed at which the wave's energy is propagated. Speed is a scalar quantity and in the SI system its unit is metre per second ($\mathrm{m\,s^{-1}}$). For a wave having *wavelength* λ and *frequency f*, its speed c is given by

$$c = f\lambda$$

■ **TIP** When using the equation $c = f\lambda$, the unit of speed must involve $\mathrm{s^{-1}}$ if the frequency is in hertz.

weak nuclear force: a force within the nucleus, acting over a range much shorter than that of the *strong nuclear force*, and having a much smaller relative strength. The weak nuclear force is responsible for the control of nuclear decay.

weight: the force acting on a mass due to a *gravitational field*; its SI unit is the newton (N).

■ For a mass m kg in the Earth's gravitational field of field strength $g\,\mathrm{N\,kg^{-1}}$, the weight W is given by

$$W = mg$$

Note that weight is not a constant: it depends on the gravitational field strength (the *acceleration of free fall*).

■ *TIP* Weight is a force and so must be a vector quantity. However, the direction of the weight is often not stated because we assume weight acts downwards!

work: work is said to be done when a force moves its point of application in the direction of the force.

■ For a force F displaced by a distance x in the direction of the force

work done by force = Fx

When the displacement is in the opposite direction to the force, work is done on the force. The SI unit of work is the same as that of energy — the joule (J). One joule is equivalent to one newton metre (N m). Work done is a scalar quantity. If the force and the displacement are not along the same line, then the component of the force along the direction of the displacement must be used.

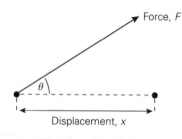

Work done by a force

Work done by the force = $Fx \cos\theta$

■ *TIP* Do not confuse the unit of work or energy (the joule) with that of the moment of a force. Both are the product of a force and a distance, but in the case of moment of a force, the force and distance are at right angles, while for work or energy, the force and distance moved are along the same line.

work done by expanding gas: the work done by a gas in expanding against an external pressure.

■ If the gas expands by an amount ΔV against a constant external pressure p (for example, expansion against atmospheric pressure), the work done ΔW is given by

$$\Delta W = p\Delta V$$

For p in pascal and ΔV in metre cubed, the work done is in joule. Work is done on the gas if it is compressed. (See also *first law of thermodynamics*.)

work function energy: the minimum energy required to eject an electron from the surface of a metal in the *photoelectric effect*.

■ If the *threshold frequency* for the surface is f_0, then a photon incident on the surface will have energy hf_0 and the work function energy ϕ is

$$\phi = hf_0$$

where h is the *Planck constant*.

X-radiation (also called 'X-rays'): *electromagnetic waves* with wavelengths in the range of about 1 nm to 1 pm, lying between *ultraviolet radiation* and *gamma radiation* in the *electromagnetic spectrum*.

■ X-rays are caused by the de-excitation of inner electrons and also by the rapid acceleration (or deceleration) of charged particles. X-rays are generated for medical use by firing a beam of high-speed electrons at a metal target. Some astronomical bodies are sources of X-rays. The most common means of detection are photographic plates, *fluorescence* and *Geiger–Müller tubes*. The absorption of X-rays depends on the *proton number Z* of the target material (absorption depends on Z^3).

■ *e.g.* X-rays are used for diagnosis of fractures and other irregularities both in medicine and in industry. Since X-ray energy is absorbed by living tissues, it does present a health hazard. However, under controlled conditions, X-radiation may be used in radiotherapy to kill tumour cells.

■ *TIP* X-rays and gamma rays are distinguishable only by their origins. X-rays are associated with the de-excitation of inner electrons or the rapid acceleration of charged particles; gamma rays are produced as a result of nuclear de-excitation.

X-ray: see *X-radiation*.

X-ray diffraction: a technique used to investigate the atomic structure of materials, including crystals and complex proteins.

■ X-rays are *electromagnetic waves* and will, therefore, show the effects of *diffraction* and *interference*. *X-radiation* has a shorter wavelength than visible light and is of the order of 10^{-10} m. This is about the same as the spacing of atoms in crystals. Consequently, atoms in crystals may act as a 'diffraction grating' for X-rays. The diffracted X-rays are detected using photographic film and the diffraction pattern is analysed to give details of crystal structure. The structure of DNA was discovered using X-ray diffraction. (See also *neutron diffraction; electron diffraction*.)

yield point: the position on a stress–strain graph at which *plastic deformation* begins and the planes of atoms within the specimen begin to move randomly.

Young modulus: the constant of proportionality between tensile *stress* and tensile *strain* for a sample of material; it is defined by the word equation

$$\text{Young modulus } E = \frac{\text{(tensile) stress } \sigma}{\text{(tensile) strain } \varepsilon}$$

Since strain has no unit, the unit of the Young modulus E is the same as that of stress, i.e. $N\,m^{-2}$ or Pa.

TIP For many solids, the Young modulus is a large number (steel, $2 \times 10^{11}\,Pa$; glass, $6 \times 10^{10}\,Pa$). Areas of cross-section are often in mm^2. Do be careful with powers of ten when doing calculations involving conversion of mm^2 to m^2.

Young's two-slit experiment: see *two-source interference*.

zero error: a systematic error that may occur in any instrument with a scale that consistently gives a reading other than zero when the quantity being measured is zero.

■ A zero error cannot be eliminated by averaging repeated readings. (See also *uncertainty*.)

Appendix A

Summary of quantities, symbols and units

This list gives the symbols and units of the quantities that are likely to be met in an AS/A2 physics specification. The list cannot be totally comprehensive and there may be some quantities that do not appear in a particular specification.

Quantity	Usual symbol(s)	Unit	Vector/ scalar
acceleration	a	m s^{-2}	vector
acceleration of free fall	g	m s^{-2}	vector
activity	A	Bq	scalar
amount of substance	n	mol	scalar
amplitude	x_0, y_0, a	m	scalar
angle	θ	rad, °	scalar
angular displacement	θ	rad, °	vector
angular frequency	ω	rad s^{-1}	scalar
angular speed	ω	rad s^{-1}	scalar
area	A	m^2	scalar
Avogadro constant	N_A	mol^{-1}	scalar
binding energy	E_b	J	scalar
Boltzmann constant	k	J K^{-1}	scalar
capacitance	C	F	scalar
Celsius temperature	θ	°C	scalar
charge	q, Q	C	scalar
decay constant	λ	s^{-1}	scalar
density	ρ	kg m^{-3}	scalar
displacement	s, x	m	vector
distance	d, x	m	scalar
electric current	i, I	A	vector
electric field strength	E	N C^{-1}, V m^{-1}	vector
electric potential	V	V	scalar
electric potential difference	V	V	scalar
electromotive force	E	V	scalar
electron mass	m_e	u, kg	scalar
elementary charge	e	C	scalar
energy	E, U, W	J	scalar
force	F	N	vector
frequency	f	Hz, s^{-1}	scalar
gravitational constant	G	N kg^{-2} m^2	scalar

gravitational field strength	g	N kg^{-1}, m s^{-2}	vector
half-life	$t_{1/2}$	s	scalar
heating	Q	J	scalar
Hubble constant	H_0	km s^{-1} Mpc^{-1}, s^{-1}	scalar
impulse	p	N s, kg m s^{-1}	vector
intensity	I	W m^{-2}	scalar
internal energy	U	J	scalar
kinetic energy	E_k	J	scalar
length	l	m	scalar
magnetic flux	ϕ	Wb	vector
magnetic flux density	B	T, Wb m^{-2}	vector
magnetic flux linkage	$N\phi$	Wb turn	vector
mass	m	kg	scalar
mass defect	Δm	kg	scalar
molar gas constant	R	J K^{-1} mol^{-1}	scalar
molar mass	M	kg	scalar
moment of force	T	N m	vector
momentum	p	N s, kg m s^{-1}	vector
neutron mass	m_n	u, kg	scalar
neutron number	N		scalar
nucleon number	A		scalar
number	N, n		scalar
number density	n	m^{-3}	scalar
period	T	s	scalar
permeability of free space	μ_0	H m^{-1}	scalar
permittivity of free space	ε_0	F m^{-1}	scalar
phase difference	ϕ	rad, °	vector
photon energy	hf	J	scalar
Planck constant	h	J s	scalar
potential energy	E_p	J	scalar
power	P	W	scalar
pressure	p	Pa, N m^{-2}	scalar
proton mass	m_p	u, kg	scalar
proton number	Z		scalar
resistance	R, r	Ω	scalar
resistivity	ρ	Ω m	scalar
specific heat capacity	c	J kg^{-1} K^{-1}	scalar
specific latent heat	L	J kg^{-1}	scalar
speed	u, v, c	m s^{-1}	scalar
speed of electromagnetic waves	c	m s^{-1}	scalar
spring constant	k	N m^{-1}	scalar

strain	ε		scalar
stress	σ	Pa	scalar
thermal capacity	C	J kg^{-1}	scalar
thermodynamic temperature	T	K	scalar
time	t, T	s	scalar
time constant	τ	s	scalar
torque	T	N m	vector
unified atomic mass constant	u	kg	scalar
velocity	u, v, c	m s^{-1}	vector
volume	V	m^3	scalar
wavelength	λ	m	scalar
weight	W	N	vector
work	W	J	scalar
work function energy	ϕ	J	scalar
Young modulus	E	Pa, N m^{-2}	scalar

Appendix B

Formulae and equations

The following is a list of formulae and equations that you will need to learn for the AS/A2 physics examinations, since they will not be provided. There will be others that you must learn, depending on which specification you are following. The formulae and equations have been given, where appropriate, as word equations as well as in the usual symbols. Do not forget that if you are asked to write down a formula or equation, you should explain any symbols used.

acceleration	(change in velocity)/(time taken)	$a = (v - u)/t$
capacitance	(charge stored)/(potential difference)	$C = q/V$
centripetal force	mass × (speed)^2/radius	$F = mv^2/r$
charge	current × time	$\Delta q = I\Delta t$
Coulomb's law		$F = (Q_1 Q_2)/4\pi\varepsilon_0 r^2$
density	mass/volume	$\rho = M/V$
electrical power	(potential difference) × current	$P = VI$
energy	(potential difference) × current × time	$E = VIt$
force	mass × acceleration	$F = ma$
gas law	pressure × volume = (number of moles) × (molar gas constant) × (thermodynamic temperature)	$pV = nRT$

kinetic energy	$\frac{1}{2} \times$ mass $\times$ (speed)^2	$E_k = \frac{1}{2}mv^2$
momentum	mass $\times$ velocity	$p = mv$
Newton's law of gravitation		$F = G(m_1m_2)/r^2$
potential difference	(energy transferred)/charge	$V = W/q$
potential energy (change in)	mass $\times$ (gravitational field strength) $\times$ (change in height)	$\Delta E_p = mg\Delta h$
power	(work done)/(time taken)	
	(energy transferred)/(time taken)	$P = E/t$
pressure	force/area	$p = F/A$
resistance	(potential difference)/current	$R = V/I$
resistivity	(resistance $\times$ cross-sectional area)/length	$\rho = RA/L$
speed	(distance travelled)/(time taken)	$v = s/t$
transformer ratio		$V_1/V_2 = N_1/N_2$
wave speed	frequency $\times$ wavelength	$v = f\lambda$
weight	mass $\times$ (gravitational field strength)	$W = mg$
work done	force $\times$ (distance moved in direction of force)	$W = Fd$

Appendix C

Physical constants and useful data

acceleration of free fall near Earth's surface	$g = 9.81$ m s^{-2}
Avogadro constant	$N_A = 6.02 \times 10^{23}$ mol^{-1}
Boltzmann constant	$k = 1.38 \times 10^{-23}$ J K^{-1}
electron rest mass	$m_e = 9.11 \times 10^{-31}$ kg
elementary charge	$e = 1.60 \times 10^{-19}$ C
gravitational constant	$G = 6.67 \times 10^{-11}$ N m^2 kg^{-2}
gravitational field strength near Earth's surface	$g = 9.81$ N kg^{-1}
molar gas constant	$R = 8.31$ J K^{-1} mol^{-1}
permeability of free space	$\mu_0 = 4\pi \times 10^{-7}$ H m^{-1}
permittivity of free space	$\varepsilon_0 = 8.85 \times 10^{-12}$ F m^{-1}
Planck constant	$h = 6.63 \times 10^{-34}$ J s
proton rest mass	$m_p = 1.67 \times 10^{-27}$ kg
specific charge of electron	$e/m_e = 1.76 \times 10^{11}$ C kg^{-1}
specific charge of proton	$e/m_p = 9.58 \times 10^7$ C kg^{-1}
speed of light in free space	$c = 3.00 \times 10^8$ m s^{-1}
unified atomic mass constant	$u = 1.66 \times 10^{-27}$ kg